A brief review of the discovery and subsequent findings of the many interesting and worthwhile researches carried out over many years.

But what does your blood group hold for you? Does your blood group predispose you to something worrying or something exciting?

ABOUT THE AUTHOR

Hugh was a Fellow of the Institute of Biomedical Science and was made a Chartered Scientist. He worked within the Health Service as a Biomedical Scientist in Haematology and Blood Transfusion. In those years, he wrote a number of research papers and scientific articles all involving blood group serology, was an invited speaker at numerous conferences and was involved in the teaching of this discipline.

He later started his own company, manufacturing antibodies and reagents used by Blood Transfusion and Transplant laboratories.

Now retired from the commercial world, he has a diploma in Art Appreciation and a pilot's licence . He has a wife and two daughters and lives in Central Scotland but spends some time on the Island of Bute.

ACKNOWLEDGEMENTS

It is always helpful to have friends and colleagues read the raw manuscript of a book for comment, direction, and criticism. Consequently, I am indebted to the following whose input might have made the work readable, perhaps more understandable and, with a little luck, saleable.

Martyn Morrison, Gordon Roberts, Morah Coats, Dr Robert Liddle, John Cunningham and Jean Murray.

Not forgetting my wife, Elizabeth, whose honest feelings on blood groups may have shone through as she spiritedly conjured up the title of the book.

Karl Landsteiner
Discovered the ABO blood groups in 1900

CONTENTS

ONE

INTRODUCTION

"Blood is a very special juice."
Faust: A Tragedy
Johann Wolfgang von Goethe

The sun shines on the word 'blood'. It carries an air of almost spiritual significance, a word that commands veneration and reverence, a word you would not wish to abuse. It can, on occasion, be charged with emotion, but it can also be spat out in anger.

When discussing blood groups, there are only two kinds of people: those who know their blood group and those who would like to know their blood group.

Tell someone that they have a rare or uncommon blood group and watch their smile broaden as you suddenly promote them to a higher plane.

However, if truth be told, there are very few rare blood groups; uncommon blood groups, yes, but rare blood groups are certainly not a regular finding.

This book is not intended to be a textbook trawling the complexities of blood group biochemical composition; rather, it will, hopefully, be an undemanding and possibly entertaining step into a world that has attracted and fascinated the millions who know their blood group.

I am hoping that the following pages of this book will give the reader a better understanding of what the blood groups are, what conclusions have been drawn by earlier researchers and, to some degree, what you might be vulnerable to because of your blood group.

But let us start with the red blood cell since that is where your blood group resides and, to be more precise, on the surface of the red cell.

The red cell is extremely small and you could get 25 million in a 5ml teaspoon. That said, they are nevertheless extraordinarily complex and their primary role is to carry oxygen, which they have collected from the lungs, and to deliver it to tissue cells throughout the body. They then clear carbon dioxide from those cells and deliver it back to the lungs, collect more oxygen and repeat the cycle.

To accomplish this, they use haemoglobin, which can combine with oxygen and can also combine with carbon dioxide. So, the red cells are filled with haemoglobin, the protein that gives blood its exotic red colour.

The red cells could be considered as the 'vehicles' that transport that oxygen-carrying haemoglobin down the arterial super-highways to supply the oxygen to all tissues. The same red cell 'vehicles', on depositing their oxygen, collect carbon dioxide and return it to the lungs via the venous pathways.

Consider the red cell as a tissue envelope which will carry the haemoglobin and, importantly, it is this envelope that carries, on its surface, the blood groups.

The use of the word 'tissue' may make that envelope sound like a simple package but it has, in reality, a very complex structure, not one to be discussed in any detail here.

So, what do we consider common and uncommon and what are the blood groups as we know them?

The first groups to be discovered were the ABO blood groups. Much later, the rhesus groups were revealed and these are the two most important blood groups in transfusion medicine. When someone requires a blood transfusion these are the two principal factors with which the blood to be transfused must be compatible.

While they are of huge importance in blood transfusion, many researchers, over time, have also considered them as possible indicators of genetic predisposition to disease, intelligence, personality, ability, psychopathy, physical attributes and indeed, a host of other characteristics that make us who we are.

While some of these reported findings are viewed today with a smile or a grimace, many have revealed disease connections of considerable importance and some will be discussed later.

However, let us start with some basic, important facts on the ABO groups, which, as has been said, are by far the most important of the blood groups in transfusion medicine throughout the world.

They were discovered in 1900 by Karl Landsteiner,[1] an Austrian physician who described the groups A, B and C, and C later became group O. Importantly, he also determined that individuals of the same ABO blood group could almost always be successfully transfused with each other's blood.

This finding is central to the safe transfusion of blood.

He was fortunate in that members of his laboratory team had different blood groups. As he was attempting to type their bloods by cross-matching their blood serum and red cells, he was, consequently, able to obtain results he could interpret. Had they all been of the same blood type, it would have taken much longer for his work to realise a conclusion.

The same brilliant scientist also discovered the polio virus and he was awarded the Nobel Prize in Physiology and Medicine in 1930.

Two of his collaborators in these 1900 findings were Alfred von Decastello[2] and Andriano Sturli, who discovered the AB blood group in 1901, although, at that time, they did not call it AB.

The discovery of the ABO blood groups was, as has been said, of great importance, but the rhesus groups are also of significant importance. However, it took until 1939 for their presence to be discovered.

Between the discovery of the ABO and rhesus groups, several other blood group systems were discovered but little attention was paid to them as they were only of minor importance. These include the groups MN and P, but nothing more will be said of them here since I do not wish to overburden the

4

reader with too much information that is not relevant to the ABO groups.

While not wishing to overstretch the reader's understanding, it has to be said that it is now known that a considerable number of blood group systems inhabit our red cells.

To give the reader some insight into the complexities and depth of research and comprehension of blood groups, Prokop and Uhlenbruck's[3] book *Human Blood and Serum Groups* runs to over 800 pages, Race and Sanger's[4] book *Blood Groups in Man* runs to almost 300 pages, while Geoff Daniel's[5] outstanding book *Human Blood Groups* runs to over 700 pages.

However, an everyday appreciation by the public of the common blood groups does not demand such in-depth understanding.

The blood groups are attached to the red cells; you could imagine them as specific structures bolted firmly and deeply onto the wall of the red cell and these structures are referred to as blood group antigens. These antigens[*] are very specific in their construction (and complex, of course) and are, generally, made up of proteins, peptides and polysaccharides. Suffice to say, that if the immune system fails to recognise any form of antigen, it will produce an antibody against that antigen.

---

[*]   An 'antigen' is the name given to any specific genetically inherited carbohydrate on the red cell wall. It is also described as any substance which can cause the immune system to produce an antibody to it if it does not recognise it.

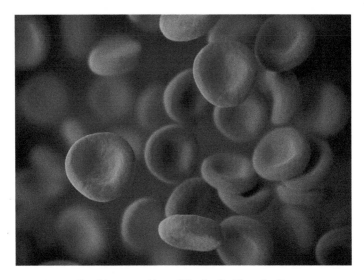

*Graphic composition of blood cells. The red cell, a
concave disk shape to give maximum surface area.*

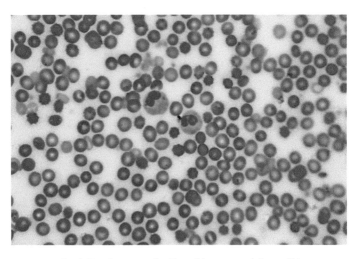

*Blood film showing red cells and leucocytes (white cells).
The blood film has been stained.*

To be a bit more specific, the A antigen is made up of a dominant sugar N-acetyl-D-galactosamine while the B antigen is made up of D-galactose.

That being rather a mouthful, is simply stating that the blood groups are made up of sugars, specifically end terminal sugars that, themselves, identify the different groups. They are spread all over the surface of the red cell and around 800,000 inhabit each cell.

So, if you are group A you will have N-acetyl-D-galactosamine attached to your red cells, while if you are group B you will have D-galactose attached.

If you are group AB, you will have both sugars on your red cells.

If you are group O you will have neither of these sugars on your red cells.

These are just sugar forms that can attach themselves to the red cells.

We are all aware that our blood is precious to us; even in a minor bleeding episode from a cut we are anxiously reaching for a bandage or sticking plaster.

Blood does not recognise racial differences. While appearances, speech and mannerisms often do, circulating blood shows no difference from one race to another and compatible blood flowing into a circulation from a racially different source is made welcome by the recipient.

A lesson to be learned here?

TWO

ABO BLOOD GROUPS

"Blood will tell but often it tells too much."
Don Marquis

As has already been said, this is the most important of the blood group systems. There are four groups in the ABO system – A, B, O and AB – and it is within the properties of these groups that transfusion safety lies.

In the United Kingdom, the distribution of these four groups is as follows:

Table 1. Percentage distribution of the ABO blood groups in the UK[6]

A	B	O	AB
38	11	48	3

The distribution of these blood groups can vary considerably throughout the world, and an example of this variation can be found in India, where group B individuals are almost as common as group O.

In view of the significant numbers of immigrants into

the USA by Europeans, the reader will not be surprised to learn that the percentage distribution for the four groups in the USA is very similar to that of the UK. Minor differences can be noted within individual USA state statistics, but the following is representative of average findings.

Table 2. Percentage distribution of the
ABO blood groups in the USA[7]

A	B	O	AB
40	11	45	4

The importance of Landsteiner's research was that it immediately made blood transfusion primarily safe when the same blood type was transfused, and as time has elapsed since his findings, blood transfusion has become an everyday safe practice.

His findings show that in the UK, group AB is the least common. But there are other factors to take into consideration before we decide which groups should be declared common and uncommon and, of more relevance, which are more in demand. More to come on this later.

So, what makes someone blood group A, B, O or AB, and what is the component that defines this label?

As has already been said, these components are called antigens, so if you are group A your red cells carry the A antigen, and similarly, group B carries the B antigen and group AB carries both antigens.

The A or B label does not stand for anything starting with an A or B; these two letters were simply chosen by Landsteiner as he had to call them something.

He did in fact, initially, call the groups A, B and C, but later C was changed to O.

As has already been said, there is a component on A and B red blood cells which is made up of oligosaccharides (sugars) and it would be a mistake here to attempt to give the reader an understanding of this complex constituent of the blood groups.

If the reader accepts that A, B and AB individuals have different markers on the surface of their red blood cells that defines them to be A or B, that will suffice. I do not wish to make this too complicated or uncomfortable for the reader and it will be sufficient to take this forward, without necessarily, confusing or boring him or her.

To understand what has made blood transfusion a safe procedure, we need to look, not only, at the blood group on the red cell, but also, at the antibodies in the plasma or serum that accompany the blood groups. Circulating blood is made up of red cells and plasma and if a sample of blood is allowed to stand vertically or is centrifuged, the red cells will sediment down, leaving a yellowish fluid which is called plasma. Normal blood contains around 45% red cells and 55% plasma or serum. It carries water, proteins, and indeed, all the nutrients the tissues require. It also contains antibodies.

The human body comes equipped with naturally occurring antibodies and an immune system that is keen to manufacture more antibodies, when called upon, to some new protein. This protein can be from a bacterial or viral origin, or indeed,

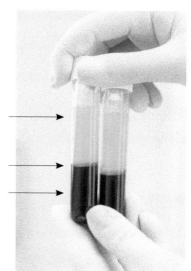

Plasma. Called plasma when an anticoagulant has been used. Called serum when the blood has been allowed to clot.

White cells and platelets.

Red blood cells.

any cell with a protein structure. Any such protein structure can also be called an antigen.

You could imagine antigens as common steel hexagonal nuts; they come in endless sizes and with different threads. When the immune system is confronted with one it does not recognise, it will manufacture an antibody, which you could now imagine as a screw, to fit exactly into the antigen/nut. The immune system will construct an antibody to exactly fit with the offending antigen and that antibody will attach itself to the antigen to assist in its removal.

Antigens, or cells, when coated with antibody will be removed from the circulation. Some antibodies are so aggressive that they will destroy the cell to which they are attached.

The antibodies are there doing their job in protecting us from all sorts of possible invaders, such as bacteria or viruses, and there will be occasions when we are dependent upon them to keep us alive.

The ABO blood groups come equipped with antibodies that are naturally occurring, and remember, our antibodies are there to protect us and will attack or attach themselves to anything that is not self.

So, the antibodies involved with the ABO groups are as follows:

Table 3. Antibodies in the ABO Blood Group System

Blood Group	A	B	O	AB
Antibodies in the plasma	Anti-B	Anti-A	Anti-A + Anti-B	None

It is now obvious that the anti-B in the plasma of the group A individual will attack and attach itself to group B red cells and the anti-A in the plasma of the group B individual will attack and attach itself to group A red cells.

Anti-A and anti-B antibodies can attach themselves to the red cell surfaces of different red cells, pulling them together in a clumping fashion. This clumping is properly called 'agglutination'.

If this takes place, the attack can be quite violent and the destruction of the red cells will be comprehensive and the cells will be removed from the circulation.

Consequently, this is how blood grouping is carried out in the laboratory. The scientist carrying out the grouping is

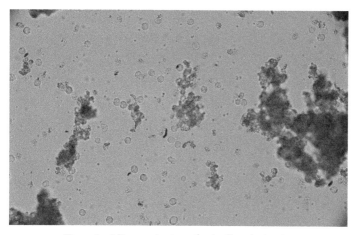

Figure 1a. Microscopic view of red cell agglutination

B Negative (-ve) Blood Group

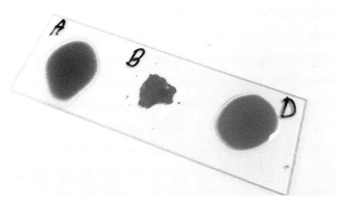

Figure 1b. Macroscopic slide view of red cell agglutination

*No agglutination with anti-A nor
anti-D but agglutination with anti-B
Patient is consequently blood grouped as B Negative*

equipped with anti-A which was acquired from a group B donor and anti-B which was acquired from a group A donor.

A tile with two circles is used. One circle has a drop of anti-A added and the second circle a drop of anti-B. A drop of diluted blood (diluted in saline) is added to each circle. The tile is then gently rocked, and since the anti-A and anti-B are usually very potent, the agglutination results can be read within a few seconds.

When agglutination occurs, the antibody clumps large numbers of red cells gathered together and the reading can be made macroscopically.

In any routine blood grouping laboratory these tests are carried out at least twice with a second scientific staff member checking the first set of results. Often, the second set of groupings are made in tubes rather than on a second tile. This allows for any discrepancies to be investigated.

The tile set-up is as shown in Figure 2.

So, it follows that:

Group A individuals can only be transfused group A or O blood.

(Their anti-B will have nothing to attack.)

Group B individuals can only be transfused group B or O blood.

(Their anti-A will have nothing to attack.)

Group AB individuals can be transfused group AB, A, B or O blood.

(They have neither anti-A nor anti-B; they can receive any group.)

Group O individuals can only be transfused group O blood. (Their anti-A and anti-B will attack A, B or AB cells.)

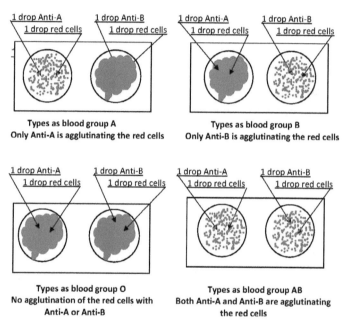

Figure 2. Tile reactions when blood is added to anti-A and anti-B

It is known that some newborn do already have some antibodies other than those passed from the mother. However, the immune system of the newborn is, generally, in a state of studying 'self' and will only start producing antibodies once the immune system is satisfied with all of what is self.

Consequently, the infant's own ABO antibodies, anti-A and anti-B are, usually, only found some months after birth. That brief period while the immune system is determining 'self' is covered by maternal passive immunity.

After that, the immune system will be prepared to defend the body against any foreign protein that gains entry to the body's tissues by manufacturing an appropriate antibody.

The antibodies anti-A and anti-B are often noted as naturally occurring antibodies. A little more will be said about this later.

Monoclonal antibodies are now used for ABO typing and, again, a little will be said about them later. While manual procedures have been described above for the typing of blood groups, many laboratories are now equipped with larger automated blood grouping equipment.

So, when all is said and done, in the ABO groups, group O is common with group A not far behind. Groups B and AB are just a bit less common.

Nevertheless, blood groups seem to be designed to generate complications and perplexing puzzles as it was discovered that blood group A could be sub-divided to types A_1 and A_2. Indeed, 20% of individuals typing as blood group A can be appropriately typed as blood group A_2. Generally speaking, this sub-typing has little relevance and the blood donation cards of the A_2 donor simply carry A as the donor's blood group.

I hate to add that you can also get A_3, A_4 and a host of other sub-types of the blood group A, but all of these are quite uncommon. Blood group B also has a number of sub-groups, but they are not very common and the casual reader should now just forget about these sub-groups of A, B and AB.

Before the discovery of DNA, the ABO groups played a major role in paternity suits and forensic science.

Since the blood groups are inherited, the following shows how children get their blood groups from their parents. Each biological parent will donate one of two ABO genes* to their offspring. In genetic terminology the A, B and O are referred to as alleles and the child receives one allele** from each parent.

ABO Genes:

> Group O will have ABO genes as
> O and O
> and can only donate O.

> Group A will have ABO genes as
> A and O or A and A
> and can donate A or O.

> Group B will have ABO genes as
> B and O or B and B
> and can donate B or O.

> Group AB will have ABO genes
> as A and B
> and can donate A or B.

---

* The ABO gene is located on a chromosome (chromosome 9) which is described as a unit of heredity.
** An allele is one of two or more structures of a given gene variant.

It follows from the above that the child will inherit as follows:

Mother group O
will have O and O
and can only pass O to child.

Father group O
will have O and O
and can only pass O to child.

Child can only be group O,
cannot be group A, B or AB.

Mother group O
will have O and O
and can only pass O to child.

Father group A
will have A and O or A and A
and can pass A or O to child.

Child can be group A or group O,
cannot be group B or AB.

Mother group O
will have O and O
and can only pass O to child.

Father group B
will have B and O or B and B
can pass B or O to child.

Child can be group B or group O,
cannot be group A or AB.

Mother group O
will have O and O
and can only pass O to child.

Father group AB will have A and B
and can pass A or B to child.

Child can be group A or group B,
cannot be group O or AB.

* * *

Mother group A
will have A and O or A and A
and can pass A or O to child.

Father group O
will have O and O
and can only pass O to child.

Child can be group A or group O,
cannot be group B or AB.

Mother group A
will have A and O or A and A
and can pass A or O to child.

Father group A
will have A and O or A and A
and can pass A or O to child.

Child can be group A or group O,
cannot be group B or AB.

Mother group A
will have A and O or A and A
and can pass A or O to child.

Father group B
will have B and O or B and B
and can pass B or O to child.

Child can be group A, B, AB or group O.

Mother group A
will have A and O or A and A
and can pass A or O to child.

Father group AB
will have A and B
and can pass A or B to child.

Child can be group A, B or group AB,
cannot be group O.

* * *

Mother group B
will have B and O or B and B
and can pass B or O to child.

Father group O
will have O and O
and can only pass O to child.

Child can be group B or group O,
cannot be group A or AB.

Mother group B
will have B and O or B and B
and can pass B or O to child.

Father group A
will have A and O or A and A
and can pass A or O to child.

Child can be group A, B, O or AB.

Mother group B
will have B and O or B and B
and can pass B or O to child.

Father group B
will have B and O or B and B
and can pass B or O to child.

Child can be group B, or group O,
cannot be group A or AB.

Mother group B
will have B and O or B and B
and can pass B or O to child.

Father group AB
will have A and B
and can pass A or B to child.

Child can be group A, B or AB,
cannot be group O.

* * *

Mother group AB
will have A and B
and can pass A or B to child.

Father group O
will have O and O
and can only pass O to child.

Child can be group A or B,
cannot be group O or AB.

Mother group AB
will have A and B
and can pass A or B to child.

Father group A
will have A and O or A and A
and can pass A or O to child.

Child can be group A, B or AB,
cannot be group O.

Mother group AB
will have A and B
and can pass A or B to child.

Father group B
will have B and O or B and B
and can pass B or O to child.

Child can be group A, B or AB,
cannot be group O.

Mother group AB
will have A and B
can pass A or B to child.

Father group AB
will have A and B
can pass A or B to child.

Child can be group A, B or AB,
cannot be group O.

To further illustrate how inheritance of the ABO blood groups materialises, Figure 3 shows one pattern where the mother is group A and the father is group B.

Consequently, where a question of paternity arises, the ABO blood groups might, undoubtedly, exclude a specific male from being the father, but it cannot, unlike DNA, authenticate a specific male as the father.

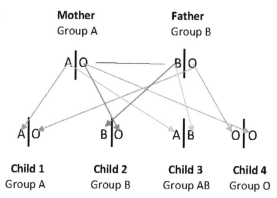

Figure 3. Demonstrating how a group A mother and group B father can have children of groups A, B, AB and O

Again, before the discovery of DNA, the blood groups were of interest in criminal forensics, but generally if the blood in question was from the suspect who proved to be group O or A, that finding was probably unlikely to be of significant use to the police or prosecution.

However, the blood group antigens on our red cells are also accompanied by a soluble antigen in all our fluids. So, if you are blood group A, you will have a soluble A antigen in all your body fluids (e.g. saliva), providing you are a secretor and four out of five individuals are secretors.

Being a secretor, or a non-secretor, has no bearing on your health (can have marginal issues), but in forensics, if the suspect perpetrator of a crime should be ABO group B or AB and a non-secretor, in concert with findings at the crime scene, that evidence might be considered as a further indication of that individual's involvement.

DNA has now superseded the use of ABO blood group findings at crime scenes.

It is of interest that, using bone extracts from the mummy of King Tutankhamen, his ABO blood group was established to be group A. This group was established using the soluble antigens extracted from his bones.

I recall a time when I was in the Special Care Nursery of the hospital and caught the glance of a paediatric consultant who was talking with a young man. A moment later, the consultant was beside me.

"Mmmmm, wonder if you could have a word with this young man, you know a lot more about

blood groups than I do."

I was immediately suspicious; this consultant had a good understanding of blood groups and I watched as he hurriedly disappeared along the corridor. I turned to the young man, knowing that I had been flushed into a possible difficult explanation scenario.

"It's my new baby," he explained quietly. "I'm wondering if he has a really uncommon blood type." I was, of course, feeling a little uncomfortable with this opening.

"What is the blood group?" I asked almost nervously.

"He is blood group A." he said as he watched my face switch to a puzzled look. "You see my wife is blood group O and I am blood group O."

I hesitated, fully realising why my friend the paediatric consultant had hurriedly disappeared over the horizon.

"How do you know you are group O?" I asked him. "Are you a blood donor, got a donor's card telling you your group?"

"No," he said, "but my mother is group O and my father is group O so I must be group O."

If he had worked that bit out, I wondered why he hadn't worked the first bit out. Perhaps he didn't want to face his conclusions of the first bit.

But in this situation who do you believe, your mother or your wife?

Either your father is not your father or...

Not sure what conclusion I ultimately offered him but, not wishing to be quoted in court, I escaped, insinuating

25

as little as possible, offering only an unintelligible and incomprehensible scientific suggestion.

Suffice to say that the ABO blood groups are of paramount importance when it comes to blood transfusion. Group O, having no antigens for a patient's anti-A or anti-B to attack, is considered a universal donor and is happily transfused to anyone where urgent blood replacement is essential. Group O plasma does carry anti-A and anti-B, but these antibodies can be neutralised by the patient's soluble antigens or diluted in the circulation.

There will be some discussion on anti-D, a rhesus antibody that can affect the newborn of some rhesus negative women, and consequently, rhesus negative blood is considered the better choice as a group O universal donor.

Almost all blood donations now have the plasma removed and the recipient receives almost only red cells.

So far, this discussion has been relative to our red cells and antibodies of the ABO system, and these may be worthy of some further clarification. It has already been stated that a 5ml spoon of blood will contain some twenty-five million red cells and each single A or B red cell will have, on its surface, up to 800,000 A or B antigens. Numbers like these tend to numb the brain, but they also illustrate the complexities of the red cell and the demands on our marrow to manufacture the cells. The marrow produces 95% of our red cell requirement and each cell is formed from a stem cell before entering the circulation as a functioning cell containing haemoglobin. Red cells are also called erythrocytes.

The marrow can be viewed as a factory unit manufacturing an incredible number of cells every second and ensuring that they are fully equipped to deal with the rigours and demands of carrying oxygen around the body.

The life of the red cell is approximately 120 days.

The immune system comes armed with a full team of able and aggressive warriors, ready and willing to deal with any hostile invaders.

The first line of defence by the immune system is our antibodies, and to be fully armed, we have B lymphocytes or B cells and T Lymphocytes or T cells.

When a B Lymphocyte bonds with a foreign antigen, it is stimulated to divide, and continue dividing, until ultimately, forming a group of cells called a clone. These cloned cells secrete millions of antibodies into the bloodstream and lymphatic system. Antibodies have all sorts of mechanisms for neutralising the foreign antigen, be it bacterial or any other invader. B cells recognise an inexhaustible number of antigens, and, again, the term 'factory output' comes to mind.

The production, maturation and functioning of T and B cells is particularly complex and too challenging to simplify in this review. Perhaps suffice to remark upon them and trust that they will continue to perform as described for each of us.

The antigens A and B, that have been described, have also been known for many years to be widely distributed in tissue cells and body fluids throughout the body.

The next most important blood group is the rhesus system.

THREE

RHESUS BLOOD GROUPS

"You know you are old if they have discontinued your blood type."
Phyllis Diller

The first hint and understanding of the rhesus system emerged from the USA in 1939 when Levine and Stetson[8] studied the blood of a mother who, on being transfused with her husband's blood, had experienced a serious transfusion reaction. In those days, it was usual that if a woman needed a blood transfusion, it would be her husband who would donate the blood.

This mother had given birth to a stillborn infant which had died of Haemolytic Disease of the Newborn (HDN), also known as Haemolytic Disease of the Newborn and Foetus (HDNF) and, earlier, Erythroblastosis fetalis.

Since the mother was group O and her husband was also group O, she should not have experienced a transfusion reaction and the serologists were puzzled and had to fully investigate.

On investigating her blood, they discovered an antibody

in her serum which they considered likely to have caused the HDN and perhaps the transfusion reaction as well. They subsequently tested this antibody against 104 group O samples. It reacted strongly with the red cells of 80 of the 104 indicating to them that they had discovered another, so far unrecognised, blood group.

Meantime, Landsteiner and Wiener in 1940 and 1941[9], had been experimenting with the immunisation of rabbits and guinea pigs with *Rhesus macaque* monkey red cells. They were keen to see what antibodies the rabbits or guinea pigs would develop to the monkey's red cells.

One of the rabbits did develop an antibody to the monkey red cells and they tested it against the blood cells of a large number of New York Caucasians. They found that it reacted with 85% of the samples which, they believed, was essentially revealing a new blood group system.

This new blood group was therefore named 'rhesus' after the monkey and they called the antibody involved 'anti-D' in some keeping with previous blood group lettering.

In the UK, 83% of the population responded with a positive reaction to the antibody while 17% responded negatively.

It was shown that the ABO and rhesus blood groups were not linked and were inherited independently of each other.

Consequently, where in *Table 1* we had four blood groups, we now must open this up to eight, and the following is a good indication of the average percentages found in the UK.

Table 4. Percentage distribution of the ABO and rhesus blood groups
in the UK

Blood Group	A+	A-	B+	B-	O+	O-	AB+	AB-
% in UK	31	7	9	2	41	7	2	1

However, in time, it was further revealed that this new rhesus system was not dependent upon only one antigen (the D antigen), but it involved a series of others which would massively complicate this blood group system.

However, I will not, at this point, attempt to elucidate the rhesus complexities; rather, I will stick with the most important aspects of this system, anti-D and the correspondent D antigen.

The 85% individuals shown to react with the antibody Landsteiner and Weiner recovered from the rabbit were simply declared 'positive', and, very quickly, it was shown that it and the antibody Levine and Stetson had recovered from the woman who had reacted so strongly to her husband's blood, were more or less identical.

So, that woman was D negative or rhesus negative while her husband was D positive or rhesus positive. The terminology was Rh and later RhD, but we will persist with D positive and D negative.

Before the discovery of the rhesus blood group system, a condition termed Erythroblastosis fetalis, observed in some newborn where there was clear evidence that anaemia and red cell destruction had occurred, had been recognised. It was soon concluded that some infants born to rhesus negative women could suffer from a form of haemolytic disease as in the case of the woman investigated by Levine and Stetson,[8] and it was later determined that Erythroblastosis fetalis, now termed Haemolytic Disease of the Newborn (HDN), was caused by the anti-D antibody. While some infants were only mildly affected, for others it could be life-threatening and even result in the death of the infant.

Some information on how anti-D develops in the rhesus negative woman would be useful at this point.

If a mother, who is D negative, is pregnant to a partner who is D positive, and the foetus is donated a D positive antigen by the father, its red cells will of course be rhesus positive or D positive. If some of these foetal red cells find their way into the mother's circulation, her immune system might develop Anti-D since the D antigen is foreign to her immune system.

However, with a first pregnancy, anti-D is unlikely to develop since the point at which the leakage of foetal red cells into the maternal circulation usually occurs is when the placenta is subject to some trauma. This is likely to arise at the time of the delivery of the child and placenta.

Consequently, the first pregnancy is unlikely to be affected by maternal anti-D since it has yet to be developed by the mother's immune system.

But given some time, her immune system may produce an anti-D which might seek to affect the next pregnancy should it prove to be D positive.

It has to be said that not all women in the same scenario

develop anti-D, and indeed, only a small number of these women become sensitised.

If sensitisation does occur, further pregnancies are likely to intensify the strength of the maternal anti-D.

HAEMOLYTIC DISEASE OF THE NEWBORN (HDN)

When the above set of circumstances are met, HDN will occur if the infant is rhesus positive (D positive). When the baby is born it may be anaemic due to the loss of red cells and it is likely to have some jaundice. Many newborn, not affected by HDN, might develop a light jaundice at birth but the infant suffering from HDN can develop a deeper jaundice which can have serious consequences.

The jaundice is created by the breakdown of the baby's red cells with the maternal anti-D being responsible for that destruction. The jaundice is essentially, circulating bilirubin, a by-product of the breakdown of the haemoglobin which has been released from the red cells.

Unfortunately, bilirubin is a toxic product and will attach to the soft ganglia of the brain. Consequently, it is important to ensure that a build-up of bilirubin in the infant's circulation is averted.

When an infant looks jaundiced, frequent bilirubin and haemoglobin blood checks are carried out. A high bilirubin, with a lowered haemoglobin, will require medical intervention.

It was known that sunlight could denature bilirubin and, if a baby was wholly exposed to sunlight, it was established that some control of a rising bilirubin could be achieved. Consequently, jaundiced babies have a light source placed within the crib bassinet, and with the baby's eyes shielded, the light is left on all day. This system, while extremely helpful, especially with infants where HDN was not the problem, could not always control the excessive bilirubin level often found in infants suffering from HDN.

When such a bilirubin level does arise, there will be a point at which a decision to exchange transfuse the baby might have to be considered.

An exchange transfusion involves a unit of fresh rhesus negative whole blood, where 10 or 20ml of blood is injected through a cord vein into the infant, followed by 10 or 20ml being withdrawn from the infant and discarded. This process of injecting fresh blood and withdrawing damaged blood is repeated until it is considered that enough infant blood containing bilirubin and anti-D antibody has been removed from the infant's circulation with a volume of fresh, healthy blood now circulating.

This process is possible through a three-way valve fitted to the injecting syringe which allows the blood to be drawn from the blood bag, then injected into the infant, then drawn from the infant and that volume ultimately rejected to a basin. Where the maternal antibody is very potent, there might be a requirement to exchange transfuse the infant more than once.

On a very rare occasion, an infant suffering from severe HDN might be in danger of dying before birth.

In 1963 the first intraperitoneal transfusion was carried out with the foetus in situ. In this procedure, the transfused red cells are deposited into the peritoneum of the infant via a needle passed through the uterus wall.

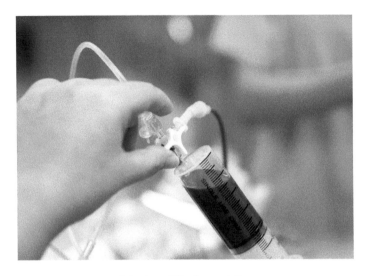

Injection of blood to an infant

These transfused red cells are, ultimately, transported from the foetal peritoneal cavity to the foetal circulation via the lymphatic system.

Later, around 1981, with more sophisticated surgical equipment, obstetricians were able to connect a blood line directly into an umbilical vein and directly transfuse a foetus suffering from severe HDN.

As far back as the 1960s, several blood bank scientists were researching the possibility of injecting anti-D into the maternal circulation of Rh-negative women who had given birth to Rh-positive infants in order to prevent the sensitisation of the mother and possible HDN.

The first report of a positive outcome of this theory was by Clarke and Sheppard[10] in a letter to the *Lancet* in 1965. They found that all 27 rhesus negative women, who had given birth to a rhesus positive infant and intravenously injected with anti-D after the birth of that infant, failed to produce anti-D.

It was, originally thought, that this anti-D was eliminating the D positive red cells in the maternal circulation thus preventing a response from the maternal immune system. However, it was later established that the anti-D, in attaching itself to the D antigen, simply masks the foreign antigen from the maternal immune system.

Soon afterwards, the introduction of intravenous prophylactic anti-D became a standard practice for all rhesus negative women who had given birth to a rhesus positive infant.

This research work is a remarkable success as very few rhesus negative women are now sensitised to produce anti-D antibody.

Before the introduction of prophylactic anti-D, around 0.45% of all pregnancies were shown to have rhesus antibodies which could affect the foetus[11], and this has now declined to almost zero.

During pregnancy, the foetus is foreign to the maternal immune system and can consequently, be vulnerable, although the placenta can help protect it by preventing the ingress of certain antibodies.

In blood banking, we consider two major categories of antibodies, IgM and IgG.

Relative to pregnancy, IgM is a large antibody and cannot cross the placental barrier, while IgG is much smaller and can cross the placenta with ease and gain access to the circulation of the foetus.

The ABO antibodies are generally IgM and while anti-D can be IgM, it is generally IgG.

If you were left with the feeling that the ABO blood groups could be complicated, they are simple when compared with the rhesus system.

While not anxious to make the rhesus system too complicated and boring, I nevertheless must add that, as well as D, there are principally four other antigens involved denoted by letters C, E, c and e. The corresponding antibodies, anti-C, anti-E, anti-c and anti-e, as well as anti-D, are all involved and they can all cause considerable difficulties when any are present.

While they can affect the foetus, they are usually weaker and it is almost always only anti-D that presents a serious problem.

Just as we encountered sub-groups for the A and B blood groups, so we also have a sub-group for D, and the rhesus blood group D^u has been recognised.

As has been said, the rhesus system is even more complex than the ABO system with endless variants and endless antibodies, generating disturbing nightmares for the student grappling with an understanding of its intricacies.

However, again, I am not anxious to trawl down to some of these depths as the casual reader is unlikely to gain anything further of value.

Perhaps it is just as well that group O is the most common since it can be transfused to anyone as it does not carry the A or B antigens.

So, group O is considered as universal donor and O rhesus negative is an even better universal donor since it does not carry the D antigen that might sensitise the rhesus negative female who needs an urgent transfusion outside the safe confines of the hospital.

I recall attending a conference where the lecturer described the blood findings of a teenage rhesus negative pregnant girl.

Despite claiming to have never been pregnant nor transfused, she had a very potent anti-D (IgM as well as IgG) in her blood which was very likely to threaten the life of her foetus if it was to be D positive.

On examination, it was clear to the obstetric staff that she had, indeed, never been pregnant and she was unlikely to deny ever having been transfused. She was an intelligent girl from a good family and it all seemed rather strange since anti-D can only be produced by the immune system as a consequence of exposure to D positive red cells; nothing other in nature has ever been shown to mimic the D antigen.

This was, of course, both concerning and puzzling, and the obstetrician ultimately had a lengthy and exhaustive dialogue with her expressing his concern for her foetus. He was also aware that there was something she was not telling him.

After some considerable persuasion, she ultimately

revealed to him that she and her boyfriend had been exchanging blood with each other. She would draw 5ml of his blood into a syringe and he would then inject that syringeful of his blood into one of her veins.

He, in turn, would then draw 5ml of her blood into the syringe and she would inject that into one of his veins.

He was, of course, rhesus positive and his D positive red cells had sensitised her to produce anti-D. Since they were wrapped up in this almost religious conviction, they had persevered with the ritual over some months. Of course, further injections of his red cells only served to further stimulate her immune system to manufacture a more potent anti-D.

They had the conviction that this pledge of the inter-blood transfusing of each other would fully bond and crystallise their loving commitment to each other.

It was unfortunate that they did not understand the downside of their actions.

I never learned the outcome of this pregnancy.

FOUR

OTHER SEMI-IMPORTANT BLOOD GROUPS

"You did thirst for blood, and with blood I fill you."
Inferno, Dante Alighieri

Unfortunately, the story does not end with the ABO and rhesus groups.

In the confusing and perplexing world of blood groups, we encounter a host of less commonly known systems all located on the red cell. Fortunately, it is only on a very rare occasion that some of these blood group systems present a clinical problem.

This is also where the simple use of designated letters to classify the system was abandoned and researchers chose to donate names to the blood groups of their choosing. Consequently, this has resulted in a bewildering assortment of characters in the nomenclature and classification of these groups.

To begin simply, there is what has been called the nine main blood group systems and they are:

Table 5. The nine main blood group systems

System name	Antigens present	Year discovered	Discovered by
ABO	A, B, H	1901	Landsteiner[1]
MNSs	M, N, S, s	1927	Landsteiner and Levine[12]
P	P1, P2	1927	Landsteiner and Levine[13]
Rh	D, C, c, E, e	1940	Landsteiner and Wiener[9]
Lutheran	Lu^a, Lu^b	1945	Callender, Race and Paykoc[14]
Kell	K, k	1946	Coombs, Mourant and Race[15]
Lewis	Le^a, Le^b	1946	Mourant[16]
Duffy	Fy^a, Fy^b	1950	Cutbush and Mollison[17]
Kidd	Jk^a, Jk^b	1951	Allen, Diamond & Niedziela[18]

The casual reader might be interested to know a little more about some of these lesser-known blood groups, but nothing will be achieved by any in-depth discussion on them, so I will keep the technical input to a minimum.

However, it is important for the reader to know that these groups exist and that they might crop up in someone's life, especially if they have a rare or uncommon group or the difficulty in finding compatible blood arises.

New blood groups are only discovered when an

individual's immune system produces an antibody and the following is an example of how this can occur.

Let us take someone who has the Kell blood group KK. This Kell group is inherited where the parents are both usually Kk.

Mother group Kk
will be K and k
can pass K or k to child.

Father group Kk
will be K and k
can pass K or k to child.

Child can only be Kell group kk, Kk or KK.

If the child is KK, this only occurs in 0.2% of the population, so it is quite uncommon. The Kell group kk is very common at almost 91% of the population.

Kk is present in approximately 9% so someone who has the Kell blood group KK does, indeed, have a rare blood group.

Another way to look at this inheritance can be seen in the family tree shown in Figure 4.

If the individual who has inherited the Kell group KK requires a blood transfusion for any reason, it is very likely that he or she will receive blood which is carrying the k antigen. If pregnant, the foetus's red cells will very likely have the k antigen which might leak into the maternal circulation and sensitise the mother to produce anti-k.

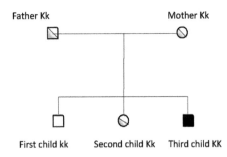

Father Kk   Mother Kk

First child kk   Second child Kk   Third child KK

Figure 4. Example family tree where the KK group can occur

If transfused, the immune system could then identify the transfused red cells as being foreign and the individual could develop an antibody to the k antigen. The transfused red cells, on this occasion, may survive since the immune system will take a little time to develop the anti-k, but should a further transfusion at a later date be required, the laboratory cross-matching the blood will then detect the antibody and find it necessary to search for KK type blood.

On the other hand, the KK patient's immune system may not make an anti-k and the problem might not rear its head. However, the antigens of the Kell system are the most immunogenic after ABO and rhesus.

The above set of circumstances, triggering the immune system's response to what it considers as a foreign blood group protein, is the manner by which all blood group antibodies are developed other than the ABO, since they are naturally occurring.

When a new, previously unrecognised, antibody is discovered, it can be harvested from the donor/patient and used by a blood group serologist, usually within a blood transfusion service, to determine what the positive rate is in the general population.

While I have noted nine blood group systems above, Daniels[5] stated in his book of 1995 that there were 23 genetically discrete blood group systems and over 250 authenticated blood group antigens. By June 2021, the International Society of Blood Transfusion Working Party for Red Cell Immunogenetics and Blood Group Terminology, in maintaining their official record of all currently recognised blood group systems, showed a total of 43 systems containing 345 red cell antigens.

Where will it all end?

While I have lamented on the perplexing assortment of names assigned to blood group systems by the researchers who had discovered them, The International Society of Blood Transfusion Working Party have created a system of numbers which have been allocated to each blood group system to bring some orderly classification to the nomenclature.

In this system, the ABO Groups are 001, MNSs 002, P1PK 003, Rh 004, etc. While this brings about a more logical and practical nomenclature, it is not quite as warm and sentimental as Kell or Duffy, etc.

Laboratories are often staffed with individuals whose sense of humour can, at times, stretch the imagination and it only takes a careless remark to activate that creative ingenuity.

The young Medical Laboratory Scientist had commented smugly that no one had been able to make a monkey out of him.

Just at that time, a local laboratory had been using rhesus macaque blood in some experimental work and, since they were using only the plasma from these samples, our request for the red cells was met favourably. At that time, we had a liquid nitrogen store of rare human red cells and the addition of rhesus macaque red cells was considered useful since they would help identify certain rare rhesus antibodies.

There was an excess supply of the monkey red cells and it was considered an important lesson to slip an aliquot of these red cells into the daily routine ante-natal groupings.

The sample was labelled as Mrs Macaque and the request form bore the doctor's name as Dr Gibbons.

The groupings on Mrs Macaque's sample showed her to be group AB but with an anti-A and anti-B present in her plasma.

These findings were before the introduction of monoclonal anti-A and anti-B, and the anti-species antibodies were responsible for the highly irregular results.

This was an astonishing finding for the young scientist and his enthusiasm in finding such a rare grouping knew no bounds. Further to this, the panel of red cells used to determine what the antibodies would be had also been manipulated with monkey blood to *confirm the presence of an extremely rare antibody and, indeed, blood group finding.*

While the episode was somewhat entertaining for those involved other than the young scientist, it was nevertheless a bit sad as the young scientist's enthusiastic approach to the finding was for him very disappointing since he had not discovered a particularly rare antibody.

An experienced blood bank lecturer used to emphasise 'when finding antibodies in a patient's serum you usually find sparrows before hummingbirds in this country'.

Maybe a lesson learned, maybe not?

FIVE

WHAT MIGHT YOUR BLOOD GROUP PREDISPOSE YOU TO?

"Life is priceless, so is blood."
The Girl from America, Ephantus Mwenda

THE EARLY YEARS - BLOOD GROUPS AND PERSONALITY ISSUES

It has long been the aspiration of several researchers to link the ABO blood groups to disease, psychopathy, intelligence, physical attributes, ability, personality and a host of other personal characteristics that make up our individuality.

It would be most pleasing to discover that your ABO blood group was an indication that your intellect was likely to be outstanding or that you had great athletic potential. However, by the same token, if any of this was found to be a true indicator, you might find that it implied that you had significant potential for criminal activity.

When Weiner studied the findings from this period he referred to them as 'Blood Group Mythology'.

So, what was found by these early researchers?

Schaer's[19] book in 1941 called *Character, Blood Groups and Constitution* recorded his detailed research on military personnel.

He documented that his findings had shown that persons of blood group O have, to a certain extent, a less satisfactory strength of character and personality.

He also declared that blood group B individuals were impulsive and that group A types were likely to make good goalkeepers; football coaches should take note.

In 1927 Bohmer[20] and, subsequently, Palmieri in 1929[21] found that among the criminal fraternity, there was a higher incidence of blood group B individuals.

Police constables should take note.

Kanazawa,[22] in his paper 'ABO Blood Type and Personality Traits: Evidence from Large-scale Surveys in Japan', refers to some of the work done by researchers on the influence of the ABO blood groups on aspects of human ability, etc.

One recorded that 'Many Japanese Prime Ministers have been type O' while another commented that their defence ministers were predominantly type O and AB. An Italian study stated that type Os were excellent long-distance runners, while in South Korea, type O was the best batter in professional baseball.

Where the individual competitor participated in athletics, group B was considered likely to be the best player.

Kanazawa stated, 'These can be recognised as evidence that blood type is related to physical constitution and personality.' This was stated as recently as 2020.

Several scientists considered that the ABO blood groups could be used to determine which individuals could be best fitted to their preconditioned roles in production. To this end, Asgari[23] stated 'there is a significant and positive relationship between blood groups and group participation', showing that:

Group A had the highest participation, group B had the second highest rank and group AB ranked third. He also stated that group B individuals had the tendency to work individually.

He concluded that the research results could be used as scientific alternatives to improve productivity in organisations. This paper was as recent as 2015.

O. Ben Degildim, having read what information was available to him, compiled a concise précis of what he had read:

Type O
Type Os are outgoing and very social. They are initiators, although they do not always finish what they start. Creative and popular, they love to be the centre of attention and appear very self-confident.

Type A
While outwardly calm, they have such high standards (perfectionists) that they tend to be balls of nerves on the inside. Type As are the most artistic of the blood groups. They can be shy, are conscientious, trustworthy and sensitive.

Type B
Goal-orientated and strong-minded, type Bs will start a task

and continue it until completed, and they will complete it well. Type Bs are the individuals of the blood group categories and find their own way in life.

Type AB
Type ABs are the split personalities of the blood groups. They can be both outgoing and shy, confident and timid. While responsible, too much responsibility will cause them a problem. They are trustworthy and like to help others.

Wxtp.Wordpress.com/22/10/2014. Blood Types and Character features of People.

During these early years, a considerable number of facile papers were published implicating the individual's ABO blood group with specific personality issues. The greatly respected blood group serologist Wiener labelled these findings as 'blood group mythology'.

However, despite such critical comments, papers continued to appear in the same vein.

In 1973, the journal *Nature* published a paper by Gibbons[24] which probed into the role of the ABO blood groups and intelligence. Gibbons ABO typed and IQ tested 534 individuals aged 18–70 across seven villages near Oxford.

He found that the mean IQ results indicated that those of groups A_2 and A_2B returned the highest score with group O following.

Socioeconomic groups in England were also the subject of possible ABO type association when Beardmore[25] and Karimi-Booshehri in 1984 published their findings. They found that ABO group A featured significantly among the higher socioeconomic groups when compared to the other groups.

Since the subject seemed to attract readers, books were suddenly being published. In 1988 the book *You Are Your Blood Type – the Biochemical Key to Unlocking the Secrets of Your Personality*[26] was published. This book by Naomi, whom I believe had no medical background, discusses how some Japanese companies use blood groups when assessing new job applicants. His son, Toshitaka, runs the Institute of 'Blood Type Humanics', in which he says 'it is not his aim to judge or stereotype people but simply to make the best of someone's talents and improve human relationships'.

While we all have what might be described as a passing interest in blood groups and what they might mean, the Japanese are fascinated by it, and we are still seeing papers published as recently as 2021.[27]

Ruth Evans[28] summed up some of this beguilement with the subject when she penned:

> *'According to popular belief in Japan;*
> *Type As are sensitive perfectionists and good team players, but over-anxious.*
> *Type Os are curious and generous but stubborn.*
> *Type Bs are cheerful but eccentric, individualistic and selfish.*
> *Type ABs are arty but mysterious and unpredictable.'*

However, if you scan some of the other papers by Japanese

researchers you might find a different set of conclusions.

Essentially, I feel that this brief review of the publications, relative to blood groups and personality issues, is adequate for the reader to get a flavour of what was seen as important.

Importantly, it would be an error to simply scoff at what these early researchers viewed as worthy of investigation and their consequential conclusions of what could be linked to the ABO blood groups.

All research is important, and findings that exclude an issue or ones that others cannot support by their researches, also contribute to knowledge and understanding.

BLOOD GROUPS LINKED TO DISEASE

Cancer. From the many papers published on malignancy, there can be little doubt that group A individuals are marginally more likely to suffer from a cancer than group O or B.

It must be emphasised that this finding, while statistically significant, is still only of minor significance and the group A reader should not stress over this finding.

The A antigen may play a role on the occasion that the immune system fails to react to a tumour cell, possibly recognising it as self.[29]

Gastric ulcers. Group O individuals are more likely to suffer from gastric ulcers, peptic or duodenal than any of the other groups. For those who are non-secretors, the bad news is that they are even more likely to suffer from these conditions.

The results indicating that group Os are more vulnerable to gastric ulceration problems have been comprehensibly supported through many accepted publications. Again, the group O reader should not stress over this finding.

Bleeding disorders. There are also several papers using sound scientific methods showing that those of group O are more likely to bleed compared to those of the other groups.

Relative to this, it has been shown that a significantly lower expression of the von Willebrand factor (one of the coagulation factors which plays a vital role in clotting) in group O individuals readily accounts for this finding.

Bacterial infections and ABO type have been shown to be inter-related where there is progress in the recovery from disease. So, your blood group may be of profound importance when that recovery is underway.

It is therefore essential at this point, that I introduce a further letter of the alphabet which is of great significance in the ABO blood grouping world.

That letter is H and you have to imagine H as the raw material that makes the A or B antigens, the precursor of A and B. To simplify, all red cells have a rich supply of H and, as this is used up with the production of the A or B antigens, so the H on the red cells is depleted.

Consequently, type A, B and AB red cells have greatly diminished H, having used it up making the antigens, while type O red cells, having no A or B antigens, still have a rich supply of H. The letter H does not stand for anything; it was simply used to denote this precursor.

Very often, in blood group serology, the ABO system is often referred to as the ABH system.

This little additional information on the ABO groups is essential for an appreciation of the following findings.

During the 1950s and 1960s there was widespread speculation that *Yersinia pestis* infection (plague) was specifically rampant in group O individuals. To this end, Doughty[30] had the opportunity to ABO type the remains of 213 Northamptonshire individuals interred in the 1300s. A comparison with those interred in the 1600s showed a substantial decrease in the incidence of ABO group O persons. This certainly indicated that group O individuals were especially susceptible to *Yersinia pestis*.

While Doughty did not have blood from the interred victims, he was able to determine their ABO groups by extracting blood group substances from their bones.

So, what was it that made those group O victims more vulnerable to the plague bacillus?

It was discovered that the bacillus has an H-like antigen on its cell surfaces and since group O red cells are rich in H, the immune system of those group O individuals is unable to produce an anti-H antibody to attack the bacillus.

Group A individuals, especially if they are A_1 (it has more A antigens on its red cells than A_2), have used up most, if not all, of the H and their immune system is consequently able to manufacture some anti-H.

Group B and AB, especially A_1B individuals, where H had been depleted, could also produce some anti-H.

Not all A, B and AB persons would have H completely depleted, and they too, would be vulnerable to the bacillus.

These findings confirm that antibodies in the ABO system can be, and often are, involved in our protection from certain bacteria. Of course, this is certainly not all-embracing; if it was, those of blood group AB, having no anti-A or anti-B, might have a struggle to survive; it is only another weapon in our armoury against micro-organisms.

Another naturally occurring antibody, one everyone has, is anti-T.

This antibody should not be confused with an antibody reacting with T cells or T helper cells.

If certain micro-organisms gain entry to our blood circulatory system, they are likely to bring havoc to our red cells. These bacteria sometimes have enzymes which have the ability to damage the surface of the red cell. To simplify this reaction, if part of the red cell surface is damaged, this damage will reveal the T antigen which is found in the underlayers of the red cell. In turn our anti-T will then attach itself to the damaged red cell and it will be removed from circulation.

If the bacterium is removed from the circulation, so the enzyme will disappear and the red cells that are undamaged will circulate normally.

When the gastrointestinal outbreak occurred in Scotland in 1996, caused by Escherichia coli 0157, 87.5% of the recorded deaths were group O individuals, indicating that the other groups probably had some conferred protection. However, the numbers involved were very small and limited conclusions should be made from the findings.

Berger et al[31], in 1989, looked at the relationship between human blood types and infectious diseases. They took into consideration the geographical and racial distribution of human blood groups along with the inter-reaction between the pathogen and the red cell membrane.

The following table is a small compilation of some of their findings:

Table 6. Relationship between infectious diseases and blood types

Infection	Susceptible ABO Group
Plague (*Yersinia pestis*)	O
Cholera (*Vibrio cholerae*)	O
Smallpox	A and AB
Tuberculosis	O and B
Gonorrhoea	B
Mumps	O
Salmonella	B and AB
Strep pneumonia	B

It has to be emphasised that your blood group will not necessarily fully protect you from an illness nor from some bacterial infection. It might help improve the odds of your survival but that is probably all.

The malarial parasite *Plasmodium vivax* is worthy of mention since it involves one of the main blood group systems, Duffy. While not an ABO type, Duffy is, nevertheless, an important blood type and its association with malaria has commanded significant research.

The following is an attempt to try to simplify the complex association between malaria and the Duffy blood type.

The Duffy blood group is scripted as Fy (I did say earlier that blood grouping nomenclature was a bit confusing so sorry about this) and, as there are two alleles (a and b), the usual European groups are noted as: Fy(a+B-), Fy(a-b+) or Fy(a+b+). However, Fy(a-b-) is almost non-existent in Europeans, but in West Africa this phenotype is very common and has probably originated because of mutation.

When the malarial parasite infects someone, it invades their red cells, where it multiplies. It has been established that the parasite gains access to the red cell via the Duffy antigen and, consequently, those of the phenotype Fy(a-b-) are usually protected, while the more common groups of Fy(a+b-), Fy(a-b+) and Fy(a+b+) are more likely to become infected.

This is a much-simplified version of the nature of this disease and its relation to the Duffy antigens. Considerable research has been carried out and I must point out that the mode of action by the parasite is not quite as simple as I have penned here.

Rhesus Haemolytic Disease of the Foetus and Newborn has already been described. It is, nevertheless, worth remarking that this blood group-generated condition is one which is such an incredible success story in appropriately dealing with the disease to a point where it now rarely causes damage to a newborn.

Auto-Immune Haemolytic Anaemia (AIHA). This condition is not specific to ABO, or any other blood types, but it does involve the patient's red cells and their immune system, so it is worthy of a mention.

A little information and reminder is appropriate at this point.

You will recall that the immune system of the newborn will be in a state of 'self-identification' and the infant is partly dependent on passive immunity from the mother.

To illustrate using an animal depiction:

If you have a black newborn mouse and a white newborn mouse and remove a small patch of skin from each and then transplant the black patch to the white mouse and the white patch to the black mouse, the transplants will be accepted. The black mouse will grow to maturity with a white patch on its skin and the white mouse will grow to maturity with a black patch of skin. This is because of their premature immune systems recognising the transplanted patches as self.

However, if you carry out the same process of cross-transplanting black and white patches of skin using adult mice, each mouse will reject the transplant as their immune systems develop antibodies to what is not recognised as self.

So, what has that got to do with AIHA and our red cells?

Well, for some reason there seems to be occasions when our own immune system gets confused with what is self and what is not self.

There is not always an understanding of why this happens but, unfortunately, on rare occasions, it can, and AIHA is an example of this condition.

The immune system develops an antibody against its own red cells and these cells are removed from the circulation. This results in anaemia and usually some jaundice as the haemoglobin is broken down and often the patient requires a red cell transfusion. Steroids are used to dull the immune system and fortunately, the condition can often disappear after a period of time.

This can also be the case with platelets and patients can develop an antibody against their platelets, resulting in the platelet numbers falling and bruising occurring. Platelet transfusions are often used to help with this condition.

Many researchers saw opportunities to probe the relationship between COVID-19 and blood groups, and numerous papers have been published on the subject.

Pourali et al[32], in 2020, reviewed as many published papers on the topic as they could find and were aware that many of the results were controversial. Consequently, they used a meta-analysis system for quality purposes.

Their overall estimate for the odds ratio between blood groups with COVID-19 infection and death was calculated with a 95% confidence interval.

Their findings were as shown in Table 7.

Table 7. % found infected with COVID-19

ABO Blood Group	A	B	O	AB
% Infected	36.22	24.99	29.67	9.29

The keen eyed mathematician will have spotted that the % Infected line adds to a little over 100. The data analysis and mathematics employed by Pourali et al to achieve their conclusions was particularly complex and I have presented their findings as published.

Table 8. % died from COVID-19

ABO Blood Group	A	B	O	AB
% Infected	40	23	29	8

This, of course, showed that those of group A were most at risk of infection and death, while group O individuals had a decreased risk.

A further two analyses were completed by two Chinese groups which were published in October 2020. They reported similar findings, but other reports have refuted any ABO relationship.

Taha[33] et al, on investigating 557 patients suffering from COVID-19 in Sudan, found that those who were rhesus negative were less likely to suffer from the disease than those who were rhesus positive.

The association of blood groups with infectious diseases has stimulated the interest of endless researchers to explore any relationship that might exist, and it would be easy to fill these pages with significant work and conclusions.

Suffice to say, in this brief review, that our naturally occurring blood group antibodies often play a role in keeping us safe from bacterial infection.

While your blood group might predispose you to infection or disease, unthinking colleagues can, on occasion, be a worse complaint than any ailment.

Linda had been with us for almost a month, a new student full of the excitement of working in a laboratory and soon to be blood grouping and learning lots about blood.

Like all new students, she was keen to know her blood group and this she did to find that she was O positive.

"Mmmm," she said hesitantly, "My mum and dad are both A positive, that okay?"

Having only worked with us for such a short period, she had not yet learned very much about the inheritance of blood groups and those around her immediately picked up on her knowledge deficiency and her puzzled concern that her parents were both group A while she was group O. It seemed to them too good an opportunity to neglect.

So far, the attentive reader will have gathered that group A parents can have group O children without any scandalous conclusions being interpreted.

There was a brief pause before one of the two onlookers said, "You are sure that they are A positive? I mean, they might have forgotten, it happens all the time."

"Have they given blood, got blood donor cards?" chimed in the other.

"They have blood donor cards," replied the uneasy Linda. "I've seen them but probably this is okay anyway, they are my parents, I know that."

"Maybe best just to leave it at that, don't ask too many difficult questions." And the two wandered off, leaving the anxious Linda to work through her anxiety herself.

It was the following morning and the day's laboratory business was well underway. The two staff members, who had been casting some doubt on Linda's parentage, were working together at a single bench.

Linda approached them from behind and stood between them. "Had it out with my parents last night," *she said almost angrily, "told them what we had found in our blood groups."*

The two, who were seated, spun round on their swivel bench stools, some alarm showing on their faces.

"My dad says he's looking into this and is threatening divorce if our findings are right!"

"But Linda…" started one of the two pranksters. But Linda abruptly turned away from them and disappeared into an adjoining lab, where she met me with a smile.

We could hear a very worried discussion between the two pranksters as they began to regret their actions.

"Think that did the trick," said Linda.

I had overheard the discussion on Linda's blood group the previous afternoon and had ensured that she did not go home questioning her parentage.

"Give them something to think about tomorrow morning," I had suggested as she left for home. And she did.

The two wind-up merchants also got a severe talking-to.

SIX

GEOGRAPHY OF
THE BLOOD GROUPS

*"My soul bleeds and the blood steadily, silently,
disturbingly slowly, swallows me whole."*
Fyodor Dostoevsky

Many theories have surfaced on the subject of what the first ABO blood type was. One theory proposes that blood group A is the oldest, with group B having come into existence some 305 million years ago. With subsequent mutations occurring and modification of the sugars that are present on the red cell, we ultimately acquired the four groups as we know them.

It has also been proposed, that the original blood group was AB and again, as a consequence of genetic mutations over a significant period of time, the A and B groups emerged and finally group O.

Other theories, however, contradict the above, proposing that the AB group is as recent as the sixteenth century while the other groups are tens of thousands of years old and that it is probable that the oldest group is either A or O.

The ABO blood groups are not spread evenly across the world, with considerable variances being reported. To begin with, and as a rough guide, the four groups have been linked to world regions as follows:

Group A

This group is commonly found in Central Europe, with Sweden, Denmark, Norway, and Austria showing a high percentage of the population possessing the gene.

Armenia and Norway are considered to have the highest concentration being noted as 46.3% and 41.6% respectively.

Group B

This group is more commonly found in Asia than in Europe, with approximately 11% in the UK. In India and China around 25% of the population belong to this group.

Group AB

Again, this blood group is more common in Asia, with 10% of the population belonging to it.

Bangladesh and North Korea are noted as having the highest population concentration of 16.8% and 11.3% respectively.

Group O

This group is the most commonly found group in the world. It is extremely common in South America and Western Europe, especially among the Aboriginal and Celtic peoples, and also in the United States.

Chile and Ecuador are noted as having the highest population concentration of 85.5% and 75.0% respectively.

It is of interest that some irregularities have been recorded. The Aboriginal peoples, for example, group only as O (61%) or A (39%) with no B or AB groups recorded.

The Ainu peoples of Japan record only 17% as group O while in the Philippines, with a population of 109 million, only 0.1% are recorded as being O negative.

Arthur Mourant's book[34] *The Distribution of Human Blood Groups and Other Polymorphisms* is still generally accepted as the source of world information on blood group distribution.

We know that group O is the most common group in the UK, with group A not far behind. The further one goes west in the UK the more group O individuals will be found, and the suggestion here is that the various invasions over the ages have resulted in the inflow of blood group A into the predominantly group O United Kingdom.

Firstly, the Romans arrived, setting up their garrisons throughout England and Scotland, but they were withdrawing by 410AD. However, they were followed by the Angles and Saxons and later, the Vikings, so the UK was almost certainly flooded by those of group A blood especially on the east coast.

Elizabeth Brown[35] made a study of the north of Scotland, determining ABO and rhesus groups. She found that group O frequencies were greater on the coastal areas of Sutherland, the west coast of Ross and Cromarty, Inverness-shire, and the Outer Hebrides. She also found that some of the north of Scotland districts had the lowest frequency of the B gene.

Cartwright and Milne[36] studied the ABO blood groups

of the inhabitants of the Island of Mull on the west coast of Scotland. This was principally carried out to meet a request to create a panel of emergency blood donors which could be used by the local GP medical staff where critical blood loss, consequent to an accident, was an issue.

However, in this undertaking they saw an opportunity to calculate and compare the ratio of ABO groups of those born in Mull of island parentage against those they termed as incomers.

Table 9. ABO group findings by Cartwright and Milne

Blood Group %					
	No	A	B	O	AB
Born on Mull	87	16.09	10.34	70.12	3.45
Born elsewhere	154	41.56	13.63	42.86	1.95
Total	241	32.36	12.45	52.70	2.49

The very high frequency of blood group O found in the indigenous population in the far west of Scotland would certainly indicate that the original population, Celts and, probably, Picts, were principally blood group O.

Many factors have played a role in the present-day distribution of the ABO blood groups. Early invasions by the Romans, Anglo-Saxons and Vikings, dictators seeking to invade by war, world travel established and recognised as part of everyday life, and the general acceptance of other religions and cultures in partnerships and marriage, have all played an important role in the present-day dissemination of the ABO blood groups.

Further to this, modern-day poverty and serious climate change have seen the migration of many peoples across the globe as they seek a better life in more prosperous countries.

All of this has led to the tidal wave of world ABO blood groups flooding to all parts of all countries throughout the world.

SEVEN

BLOOD TRANSFUSION HISTORY, PAST AND PRESENT

"The life of the flesh is in the blood"
Leviticus 17:11

The bible contains some hundreds of references to blood[37], some venerable, some sacrificial and some shed, but it generally proffers respect and reverence when it appears.

Ovid may have had some fixation with blood as he uses it frequently in his writing of *Metamorphoses*. Perseus uses the head of Medusa to fill Acrisius's land with serpents born from drops of her blood. Pegasus was born from Medusa's blood after she was beheaded and, when Ajax commits suicide, his blood produces a hyacinth flower.

When Jason and Medea arrive home, they find Jason's father very ill and she rejuvenates him by slitting his throat to be rid of the worn-out blood which she then replaces with a magical potion of her own creation.

Reading back to the fourteenth, fifteenth and sixteenth centuries, when bloodletting and the drinking of blood to rejuvenate were considered beneficial, it is not difficult to see why the taking of blood was deemed more appropriate than the giving of blood. In the late fifteenth century, Pope Innocent VIII was treated by his doctors with the blood of three young boys as a therapeutic measure. The blood was not a venous transfusion but was sipped by mouth until wholly consumed.

This blood from the adolescent juveniles was, at the time, reputed to have the essential essences to revitalise the beneficiary, but the outcome was not quite as beneficial as desired, and the Pope died soon afterwards. Little has been recorded on the outcome of the ten-year-old boys whose blood was used in the attempt to revive the Pope.

The drinking of blood to acquire the courage and strength from a fallen foe was strongly advocated by the Romans and the Egyptians considered blood baths a road to recovery when some recuperation and rejuvenation was demanded for the body.

History is positively filled with the fear of blood or the veneration of it. The word summons and commands reverence and sometimes dread, sometimes revenge and, sometimes, relief. It has been recommended as a remedy for palsy, lunacy, melancholia, manias, mood swings and the rejuvenation of the aged back to youth. It has been bled out to clear those 'bad humors' and relieve 'pressures on the brain'.

So, it was recognised as a formidable factor, one to be regarded and managed with great care.

The practice in the Middle Ages of simply cutting open a vein in the forearm and allowing the 'bad blood' to flow freely from the wound was a common practice.

It was also recognised in these early days that loss of blood could readily result in the death of the patient and many physicians were keen to try venous transfusions. However, acquiring a human volunteer for the blood donation was clearly going to be difficult, especially since the equipment used to transfuse the blood could only be described as primitive. Other solutions such as beer and milk were used.

In 1818, James Blundell, a British obstetrician, carried out what must have been the first successful transfusion on a young woman suffering a post-partum haemorrhage. Using a syringe, Blundell removed approximately 120ml of her husband's blood and injected it into her arm. Blundell later performed a further ten transfusions, five of which he claimed were successful.

The first vein-to-vein transfusions were from dog-to-dog and were carried out by Richard Lower, a young physician in England in the mid-seventeenth century. He partially exsanguinated one dog then directly transfused it with the blood from another dog. The dog which had been partially exsanguinated recovered well and the donor dog seemed no worse from the experiment.

At the same time, a report from Paris described a successful sheep-to-man transfusion.

In reality, a sheep-to-man transfusion, depending upon the volume transfused, would inevitably see a grossly incompatible end to the transfusion as the recipient's anti-species antibody would wholly destroy the sheep red cells. He would experience excessive rigours and become jaundiced as his organs struggled to remove the offending sheep red cells.

These events were, however, overtaken by the plague and, subsequently, the Great Fire of London, but after these terrible episodes, the medical community were again having thoughts of human blood transfusions.

In November 1667, Richard Lower and a colleague carried out a sheep-to-man transfusion on a 22-year-old man, Arthur Coga, whose brain was considered 'a little too warm'. This was carried out before Fellows of the Royal Society, and it was hoped and anticipated that an improvement would be seen in the man's psychological health by the cooling of his brain.

Silver tubes and quills were connected from the sheep's carotid artery to one of Coga's veins and he received around ten ounces (approximately 300ml) of the sheep's blood. Over a short period of time, Arthur Coga received further transfusions of sheep blood and seemed keen to emphasise that he felt well. Despite this, Coga's mental state was hardly improved, especially, since he claimed that the scientists had changed him into a sheep.

All of this made the Royal Society look foolish and the enthusiasm for transfusion therapy was seriously blunted.

In the late nineteenth century numerous milk transfusions were carried out, most with fatal consequences. Goat's milk and human milk were used, but by the late nineteenth century the drive to succeed with milk disappeared as the use of isotonic saline solutions as a successful substitute was published.[38]

If we jump forward to 1908, we will find an interesting tale which is relevant to the evolvement of blood transfusion, and it also delivered a better understanding of the coagulation system.

In New York a baby girl was born of 8lb 12oz. All looked well until at 36 hours, she was showing all the clinical signs of Haemorrhagic Disease of the Newborn. She had a subcutaneous haematoma behind her left ear spreading down to her neck and she was passing dark-coloured meconium (baby's first excretion, normally made up of cells, protein and fats, a bit like bile and passed in the first few hours of birth) which was clearly blood-stained, and she had blood seeping from her nose continuously.

The baby had been born into a prominent family of surgeons and doctors, and they recognised that the infant had little chance of survival unless she was transfused.

They then called upon the services of Alexis Carrel, a French surgeon with special skills in vein suturing, but he was most reluctant since this would require dealing with very small, fine veins.

He was, however, persuaded as the child was five days old and was clearly dying from the loss of blood.

The baby was strapped with bandages onto a table and Alexis Carrel was able to suture the baby's right popliteal vein (back of leg) to her father's left radial artery (forearm). This was carried out on a table in the dining room. It was difficult for them to estimate how much of her father's blood to pass into her vein and it was also difficult to determine how much was being transfused. So, some guesswork was used and, after a brief transfusion, they stopped. Much to their delight and relief, the baby's bleeding problems quickly ceased, her pale transparent skin changed to a brilliant red and she made a rapid and good recovery.

This surgical procedure was carried out without the use of any anaesthetics and must have been a little messy.

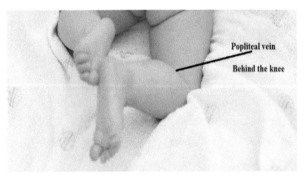

Popliteal vein

Behind the knee

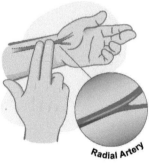

Radial Artery

Needless to say, this delicate surgery and transfusion received great publicity, being reported widely by the New York press. One article was reported as follows:

"In itself the operation is regarded as one of the most remarkable ever performed. The child was only five days old and was suffering from purpura, a disease of which little is known. Its symptoms are a weakening of the walls of the arteries so that the blood escapes from all parts of the body.

Child's father gave his blood.

Dr Carrel was called in when the life of the child was despaired of. The only possible hope lay in transfusion of blood. Dr Lambert, the child's father, volunteered to give all of his blood that was necessary to save the child and Dr Carrel undertook the operation despite there being only a slight chance of success.

He was strapped to the baby and one of his arteries was connected with one of the child's blood vessels. His blood rushed from his big healthy body into that of the child with such good effect that the baby rallied almost immediately and is now out of danger."

Carrel received the Nobel Prize in Physiology in 1912.

This medical success answered two questions: transfusing blood could readily save lives, and new, healthy transfused blood, could pass coagulation properties to the recipient.

In these early days, the quills and needles used to achieve the transfusion were still very crude and donors were, certainly, not in abundance.

A greater number of physicians and surgeons were soon attempting artery-vein transfusions and finding some success. Many were of the opinion that collected blood in some container then transfused to the patient would have abundant benefits over the direct method. However, the determination of blood to clot was a serious problem in practising this procedure.

Nevertheless, physicians were appreciating the benefits of blood transfusion and were experimenting with various chemicals to find a suitable anticoagulant.

In 1914 Hustin[39], reported that he had used a sodium citrate and glucose solution to prevent coagulation of the blood, and in 1915, Bordet reported the use of sodium citrate alone.

In 1921, members of the British Red Cross all volunteered to donate blood at King's College Hospital and this is recorded as the first blood donor session.

The first blood bank was created in Leningrad in 1932 by Dr Babdarsov and in 1937 Bernard Fantus, Director of Therapeutics, is accredited with establishing the blood bank at Cook County Hospital. He is also reported to have originated the term 'blood bank'.

Russian scientists introduced 'cadaver blood' which was drawn from accident deceased patients who had no clinical issues. Fibrinolysis (the breakdown of the fibrin layers that make up the clot) occurs 60–90 minutes after death and, at this point, blood will flow freely from the veins.

The original experimentation was carried out by Shamov,[40] who originally used dogs, with one dog being sacrificed and its blood being drawn after death as cadaveric blood, while a second dog was almost fully exsanguinated and subsequently transfused with the cadaveric blood. This was carried out in 1928 and Shamov later stated:

> "The corpse should no longer be considered dead in the first hours after death, it not only continues living in some of its parts, but also can give to those still living the gifts of great value: quite viable tissues and organs."

One considerable advantage of this procedure was that several donations could be obtained from one cadaver, around 3–4 litres, rather than the single one obtained from a living donor.

Shamov recognised that this procedure could be of great value in times of war when as he put it:

> "In conditions of war, when there are huge numbers of corpses of just killed people from whom whole barrels of viable blood can be definitely gained, the question of its use for transfusion to the exsanguinated wounded is of vital importance."

Despite this, the Red Army Medical Service did not implement the practice, but it is reported that the procedure was used in the Spanish Civil War.[41]

While Russia and several other countries were attracted to the advantages of this procedure, there was a general disquiet of the practice and the public were uncomfortable with the product. The Russians used in excess of 30,000 units of cadaver blood before abandoning the technique.

There is an odd dichotomy in our cultured logic when

it comes to the cadaver. When an accident brings about the death of an otherwise healthy body, we are at ease with harvesting the kidneys, liver, corneas, skin and a host of other healthy useful organs for transplantation. But the suggestion of procuring the healthy blood for transfusion seems to sit badly with our scruples of what is acceptable and what is not.

I wonder why?

The first blood donations were collected into glass bottles and, by that time, there was a full understanding of bacterial contamination and all equipment used for collecting and giving blood was fully sterilised.

The bottles also carried an anticoagulant into which the donor blood would run thus preventing clotting of the donated blood. Over a period of some years the anticoagulant solution was enhanced, not only to act as the anticoagulant but also, to promote the life of the stored blood.

Acid Citrate Dextrose (ACD) solutions were developed, and this preservative proved highly successful in improving the life and health of the stored red cells.

In 1975, the glass bottles were replaced with plastic bags. Plastic bags were introduced as a consequence of the breakages encountered by the military in the shipment of blood, and it was also realised that many other advantages could be achieved in using plastic.

The ease of ensuring a sterile unit of blood, the elimination of the need to re-sterilise and reuse the glass bottles, and the weight advantage all drove the transfusion services to invest in plastic. The bags were robust and would not easily damage, readily sustaining a fall without breakage.

It had to be remembered that the units of blood which might be saving lives contained an anticoagulant solution that, in volume, could prove toxic to the recipient. However, where there is a requirement for multiple units of blood to be transfused, there are now medical practices that can resolve this toxic issue.

Today, we have the National Health Service Blood and Transplant (NHSBT), the Scottish National Blood Transfusion Service (SNBTS), the Welsh Blood Service (WBS) and the Northern Ireland Blood Transfusion Service (NIBTS).

With modern-day medicine and surgery there is a daily requirement in the UK of more than 7,000 units of blood. The citizens of the UK are very generous in donating, and there are only a few occasions when supply difficulties arise.

However, less than 5% of the population are blood donors.

All blood donations are fully tested for a prescribed list of diseases. Every unit must be screened for:

- Hepatitis B – HBsAg
- Human immunodeficiency virus – anti-HIV 1 and 2 and HIV NAT (nucleic acid testing)
- Hepatitis C – anti-HCV and HCV NAT
- Human T-cell lymphotropic virus – anti-HTLV I and II
- Syphilis – syphilis antibodies

Some donations are tested for cytomegalovirus (CMV)

antibodies to provide CMV negative blood for patients with certain types of impaired immunity.

Additional tests, performed in special circumstances, include:

- Malarial antibodies
- West Nile Virus antibodies
- Trypanosoma cruzi antibodies.
- Precautions to reduce the transfusion transmission of prion-associated diseases.

These include variant Creutzfeldt–Jakob disease (vCJD – caused by the same agent as bovine spongioform encephalopathy (BSE) in cattle – 'mad cow disease') and sporadic or inherited CJD.*

When a unit of blood is donated into a plastic pack, it is immediately transported to a Transfusion Service blood bank laboratory where it is centrifuged to spin the cells to the bottom of the pack, leaving the plasma above the red cell layer.

---

* The above is taken from the Joint United Kingdom (UK) Blood Transfusion and Tissue Transplantation Services Professional Advisory Committee's 'Transfusion Handbook' on 'Tests on blood donations, screening for infectious agents'.

Whole blood is a rich source of valuable and essential blood components. The separation by centrifugation of the plasma from the red cells allows the plasma to be expressed into a separate bag for use as fresh frozen plasma (FFP) or to be fractionated into individual constituents such as factor eight, which can be used to treat haemophiliacs. Many other clotting factors can be fractionated from plasma but, generally, FFP is used where there is a requirement for the prevention of bleeding.

The triple pack shows the unit of blood after centrifugation with the packed red cells at the bottom of the pack and the plasma in the upper half of the bag.

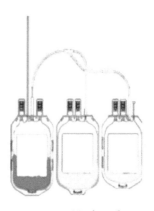

Gentle pressure on the pack of whole blood allows the plasma to be expressed across to the second and third bags which are attached to the main pack.

Figure 5. Triple pack

Often, only one secondary pack is used, and it takes the entire plasma content. It is immediately stored frozen to preserve the clotting factors and is labelled FFP.

The whole blood, with the plasma removed, is now reduced to 'packed red cells' and is stored at 4–8°C. This is suitable for patients who require red blood cells.

Platelets, sometimes called thrombocytes, are very small cell fragments made in the marrow and they are involved in ensuring that any tissue damage causing us to bleed, will be sealed. They are responsible for producing the clot that covers the wound with long fibrin threads spreading across the damage, sealing the wound.

The platelets, along with factors 11 and 12, are involved in triggering the coagulation cascade, which is a complex series of stimuli which ends with the clot being fully formed.

Some patients are found to have lower platelet counts (Immune thrombocytopenia) and may require a platelet transfusion.

Platelets can be harvested from a donated unit of blood. When the unit of blood is centrifuged, the platelets lie just at the interface between the plasma and the white cell layer. They can also be collected by apheresis, a method whereby the platelets can be collected, and all the other blood components returned to the donor.

There are myriad factors that can be extracted from plasma and some of the more important are listed below:

Albumin
Factors VIIa, VIII, IX, X and XIII
Immunoglobulin
Fibrinogen
Thrombin
Antithrombin III
Protein C

Indeed, there are a considerable number of fractionated

products that can be isolated from plasma that are of great importance in the medical world.

As has already been said, the inhabitants of the United Kingdom are generous in donating blood. They are not paid, a simple thanks and, perhaps, tea and a biscuit, and that is how it must always be.

Occasionally, an urgent appeal for donations might be televised and there is always a good response.

In many countries the donors are remunerated, but this can sadly lead to those subject to addiction, and those acutely short of money, donating. These unfortunate individuals will fail to report any illnesses and, while all donations are screened, their donation may well have to be discarded.

The blood donor system used in the UK by the Transfusion Services serves the public well. So many patients are dependent upon that gift; the life it may save will be unknown to the donor, but the recipient will be grateful.

The blood transfusion services in the UK are well managed and rarely encounter criticism. They operate with dedicated, talented teams who ensure that the blood and component stocks always meet the needs of the hospitals.

The quality of research into blood-related diseases and the development of new and innovative blood components, within these departments, is exceptional.

It tends to be generated behind laboratory doors and we hear little of the depth of experience and talents that inhabit these laboratories.

EIGHT

RARE FINDINGS IN BLOOD GROUPS

"Blood groups don't tell lies but finding and unravelling the truth within can be much more challenging."

Hugh Graham

Blood groups occasionally throw a mystery onto the table and blood group serologists just love it when one appears. Fortunately, or perhaps unfortunately, the surfacing of these anomalies tends to be infrequent, but they are exciting when they materialise.

They are usually identified because they have broken the pattern of conformity and understandings laid down by respected blood group serologists for a blood group system or they appear to have landed outside Mendel's laws of genetic inheritance.

While the occasional anomaly can bring some problems for the individual in which it has been found, they are often only of great interest to the serologists and their research.

THE CHIMERAS

A human Chimera can be described as an individual who is composed of cells from two or more individuals. Now that might, on its own, take a bit of mental unravelling but I will approach it cautiously and open the chimera door from a blood group perspective.

In 1953, Dunsford[42] reported that ABO blood grouping tests from a female blood donor in Sheffield showed a mixed field reaction of agglutination on a tile with anti-A. While many of her red cells were macroscopically fully agglutinated by the anti-A, there were many which were not and a careful separation of these two populations of red cells indicated that the unaffected red cells were, in fact, group O. After considerable laboratory blood grouping investigations, they had to ultimately conclude that this donor had, indeed, two blood groups, A and O.

This, of course, was a blood group mystery, a patient with two blood groups?

A puzzle worthy of significant investigation.

She was in good health and had not been in hospital, nor was she suffering from any illness that might shed some light on this curious irregularity.

From the various tests carried out on the donor's blood, the researchers concluded that she was genetically blood group O.

As has already been said, every group O individual will have anti-A and anti-B in their plasma or serum, but because of her group A cells this donor, while having anti-B in her serum and despite being genetically group O, had not developed anti-A.

So, where did the group A red cells come from?

The first clue was that the donor was a twin, but tests could not be carried out on that twin since it had died some months after birth.

Dunsford was familiar with a paper published some years before by Owen[43], on bovine twins, where vascular anastomoses had occurred.

To simplify this irregularity, placental vascular anastomoses is a condition where there is an anomaly of the joining of certain veins leading to a shared blood circulation twin-to-twin. Such a condition can lead to many problems, but sometimes, it can go unnoticed with the twins appearing normal.

If the twins are dizygotic (not identical) and have different ABO blood groups each twin will now have two different ABO blood groups in their circulation and since these foetal cells are primordial (early forming red cells), they can take root and continue to function throughout the life of that twin.

Such twins might each have two sets of red cells circulating, giving rise to two different blood groups in each twin.

So, three sets of conditions must be met to find someone with two blood groups:

1. They must be a twin.
2. The twins must be dizygotic with differing blood groups.
3. Vascular anastomoses must occur in the placenta.

If placental vascular anastomoses does occur, but the twins are monozygotic or dizygotic but have the same ABO blood group, the irregularity will not be revealed on ABO blood grouping.

It has to be emphasised that blood group chimerism is a very rare finding.

The young member of staff carrying out that day's routine ante-natal blood grouping tests, brought a tile along to me to show me what she thought looked irregular. While inexperienced, she had been taught to bring to the attention of a senior member of staff anything that did not conform to the normal pattern of reactions.

I looked at the tile to see two circles containing a patient's red cells, one circle with anti-A and the second with anti-B.

The circle with the anti-A was showing mixed agglutination with a major pattern of agglutinates but a small sea of free cells. There was no reaction with the anti-B.

"Don't think our anti-A is all that good," she said, "hasn't agglutinated all the patient's red cells."

That seemed very unlikely to me; the anti-A supplied to us by the Transfusion Service was always of very high quality.

The adrenalin was suddenly ripping along my tissues shouting 'Chimera' in my ears.

We set up a series of tests to determine if there were, indeed, two different populations of red cells in this pregnant patient's circulation. These tests did not take very long to complete and after around an hour we had determined that the patient had group

A positive red cells and a smaller number of group O negative red cells in her circulation.

Very occasionally, a foetus can bleed into its mother, but the indicated volume of O negative red cells in this patient's circulation ruled that possibility out.

Our excitement was palpable; we had never seen a chimera before, and this demanded a full and further investigation.

I went off to the ward to speak to the patient and sitting beside her I asked the obvious and most important question.

"Are you a twin?" She looked at me in some surprise.

"No," she said, "why do you ask that, is there something wrong?"

I hesitated; the disappointment might even have been showing in my voice.

"No, nothing wrong." I reassured her. I then went on to tell her of the interesting findings in her blood grouping results; it is not everyone who has two blood groups.

"Oh, I might be able to explain that," she said softly. "I was in a road traffic accident about a month ago. They had to give me two units of O negative blood because of the amount of blood I had lost."

I thanked her for providing an answer to our atypical findings but deep inside the disappointment was too profound for me to be over-thankful.

In the years that followed, and after many thousands of blood-grouping tests, I never did find a true chimera.

*cis*AB

I have included this group of irregular findings immediately after the Chimeras since it is a form of chimerism.

Cis in this context means 'coupling' and it is the coupling of A and B that threw yet another puzzling finding on inheritance within the ABO blood groups.

Seyfried[44] et al, reported on a Polish family where a group A_2B mother with a group O husband had two A_2B children.

In this case, the A and B antigens have been created within a single allele and can, therefore, be inherited as a single allele.

The authors noted that the B antigen in all three of these A_2B individuals was very weak and that their serum contained a weak anti-B.

A year later, a second family was reported and again, the inheritance of A_2B with the weaker B antigen was recorded.

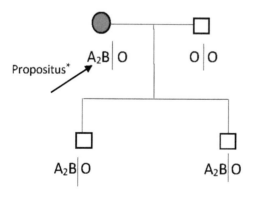

Figure 6. Family tree

---

*   Propositus. Individual in whom the irregularity has been found.

In both cases there was the presence of a weak anti-B in the patient's serum.

Soon other family studies with similar findings were reported.

Initially there was some concern that care would have to be taken in supplying compatible blood if such a patient was to require a transfusion. It is generally accepted that group AB patients can be transfused A, B, AB and O blood units, but since *cis*AB patients have a weak anti-B present, transfusion of group B or AB red cells seemed ill advised.

*Cis*AB is an extremely rare finding.

If there is likely to be any problem in the transfusion of blood regarding the donor's plasma where the recipient might not tolerate components of that plasma, present-day practices allow for the use of washed red cell units. The donor plasma is extracted from the donor bag and sterile saline is added in its place. If mixed and centrifuged, the supernatant saline can then be removed leaving the red cells without the plasma.

THE BOMBAY GROUPS

It has now been stated several times that a couple who are both ABO group O can only have group O children. However, in keeping with the occasional irregularities that try to prove the experienced blood group serologists wrong, the 1950s saw a series of group A or B children born to such couples.

This interesting finding did not come from some paternity suite but, rather, it was revealed when a railway worker in India was admitted to hospital after a serious accident. A blood transfusion was considered necessary, and a sample was sent to the laboratory for cross-matched blood. However, the laboratory found difficulty in acquiring compatible blood for him and, while he was typed as blood group O positive, an antibody in his serum strongly agglutinated any selected group O blood cells. Thirty-five blood donors were available, but none were compatible. Indeed, despite further searches, compatible blood could not be provided, and plasma was used instead. Fortunately, the patient survived the accident.

Two weeks later, a male was admitted to the hospital with abdominal stab wounds, and he too, required to be transfused. Again, compatible blood could not be found although his blood was found to be compatible with the blood of the railway accident victim.

The laboratory findings were investigated by Dr Bhende[45] of Seth G.S. Medical College, Bombay (now Mumbai), an assistant professor in the department of Pathology.

He found that their red cells ABO grouped as group O and their serum showed the presence of anti-A and anti-B but, also, another potent antibody which they ultimately concluded was anti-H. Since group O red cells are normally rich in H, the mystery of these reactions only deepened.

After the publication of Bhende's paper, other findings of the now-called Bombay groups were made and family studies and the inheritance of the anomaly were further explored.

Finding that a group O mother, married to a group A husband, had given birth to a group AB son and subsequently

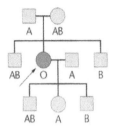

How can this be?

Figure 7. Bonbay phenotype

a group B son demanded some serological explanation. It should also be noted that in this family study, the group O female propositus (↗) was born to a group A and group AB couple. Infidelity was readily ruled out as an explanation as the clever serologists got to work unravelling the puzzle.

You might recall that the blood group antigens A and B were formed from the raw product H and that group O red cells are rich in H since it is unused.

It follows that, if that product is not available for the manufacture of the A and B antigens, they cannot be made. Several researchers all came to the same conclusion, that the individual with the Bombay group was simply unable to make the A or B antigen because of the lack of H substance and, while genetically programmed as A or B, they would appear as group O.

As a group O, their immune system naturally produces anti-A and anti-B and, having no H, it also produces anti-H. anti-H is just as strong an antibody as anti-A or anti-B.

Since all normal group O red cells are rich in H, these

individuals are not compatible with group O red cells, nor are they compatible with A or B red cells.

Consequently, the only compatible red cells that can be found are others who are also of the Bombay type. Not easy finding a unit of blood for the unfortunate Bombay individual who needs blood.

The name 'Bombay type' has remained, but this rare blood type is found in other parts of the world, and while a rare blood type, a considerable number have now been found.

It is considered likely that a gene at a locus*, independent of ABO, controls the expression of H and that the phenotype hh could arise due to homozygosity for this rare gene h.

There is also the probability that many of these fascinating types evolve as a consequence of consanguinity (inbreeding).

I was told of a young student biomedical scientist who had completed his university training and was then

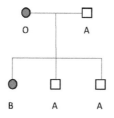

Figure 8. Family tree

---

* Locus. Is the specific physical location of a gene or other DNA sequence on a chromosome.

employed in a transfusion laboratory gaining practical experience. Some months into his 'hands-on' training he was given the accompanying family tree and asked to think carefully and write down all the possibilities of how this anomaly could arise.

His conclusions were as follows:

1.   *The labour room got the baby's blood mixed up.*
2.   *The laboratory carrying out the blood grouping made a mistake.*
3.   *The person constructing the family tree made a mistake.*
4.   *The wife of this man was playing away from home.*

I suppose any of these four conclusions could be possibilities and it may have been a bit optimistic in thinking that a young student would have brought 'Bombay' to mind. Nevertheless, he did put some thought into it.

There is a host of rare blood group findings which, in themselves, would fill many pages. I have included the above three to give a flavour of the demands some serologists are faced with in order to answer irregular findings in blood grouping.

These are, of course, the findings that help make for an exciting profession.

My phone rang and it was the receptionist.

"Got a call for you," she said, "caller sounds a bit anxious."

A moment later and I had a quiet, hesitant voice in my ear. She told me her name and I recognised it, as she was one of the nursing staff, and I knew that she had recently given birth to twin boys.

"Hello," I said brightly. "How are the twins, all okay, I trust?"

"Well." She was very hesitant, and I had a feeling I wasn't going to enjoy the call. It took her another few moments to get there.

"It's about them I'm calling." Another pause. "You reported their blood groups as group A. I'm wondering, if, if there could be some mistake, is there any way this could be wrong? I mean, well, I…"

There was a silence, so I responded as she was clearly very nervous.

"What is the problem with them being group A?" I asked, although I did have a feeling that I would recognise the problem.

"I don't see how they can be group A," she said. "I am group O and my husband is group B. I mean, it's got to be a mistake."

There was another long pause and I struggled for some words to help.

"Well, I suppose if the labour room got the cord samples mixed up. Were there any other twins delivered at the same time?"

"Don't think so, no."

"Or there could have been some error when the groupings were being done or typed up." That didn't seem likely to me, but you never know.

"Could they perhaps have some rare group, something uncommon?" She was clutching at straws and probably knew it.

I had the feeling that she wanted me to describe some rare group along the lines of what I have described in this chapter.

"Surely there could be another reason why they are group A?" She certainly was fairly insistent. "Another reason?"

I paused. She was a nurse; surely she could see a clear possible alternative logical reason but just wanted to deny it. I paused further, unsure what to say that might not be insulting.

However, I could see a way forward that might bring an answer to this difficult issue.

"Well, what I suggest, to resolve this irregular finding," careful words, of course, "is that you bring the twins in and I'll take some blood from each and we can do their blood groups again."

There was another very long pause as she thought about all that had been said.

"Well, okay, I could do that, when should I bring them in?"

"Any day next week, but let me know when you are coming."

In some ways, for me, it was not a surprise when she failed to appear with her twin boys the following week and I never did meet her again.

NINE
CROSS-MATCHING, ETC.

"The best blood will at some time get into a fool or a mosquito."
Benito Mussolini

In the regular hospital scenario, the blood bank laboratory will hold a reserve of blood units in their blood bank refrigerator to cover routine and emergency demands. The volume of blood held will depend upon the size of the hospital and the range of specialities undertaken by the medical and surgical departments.

With elective surgery, a form with the patient's details along with a clotted blood sample from the patient, will be sent to the blood bank laboratory requesting the number of blood units that is considered the likely requirement to cover the operative procedure.

This will be a request for cross-matched blood which is considered the safest call since the units to be transfused will be fully tested before being declared compatible with the patient.

Where surgery is not involved, or where the medical

department feels that there is unlikely to be an urgent demand for blood, a 'Type and Save' request will be sent to the blood bank laboratory. That sample will be blood grouped and the serum checked for blood group antibodies. It will then be held should an unexpected emergency request arise for cross-matched compatible blood.

There are occasions when a patient requires extremely urgent transfusing and, in such cases, O negative blood or type-compatible blood will be used.

CROSS-MATCHED BLOOD

This procedure is carried out where there is no desperate urgency for transfusion and where even a little time can be permitted for the compatibility tests to be completed. It can be to cover an operation later that day or the following day or where there is anaemia or blood loss, but essentially, where the patient's life will not be compromised by allowing time for the cross-matching tests to be carried out.

A sample of clotted blood will be sent to the laboratory where it will be centrifuged, and the serum and red cells separated.

The blood group of the patient will be determined and units of blood of the same group will be selected from the blood bank refrigerator.

The red cells of the blood to be transfused will be matched against the patient's serum since any possible transfusion problems (the presence of antibodies) will be found there.

When blood is donated, the needle in the donor's arm floods the donor blood down a tube and into the blood-collecting bag. When the donation is completed, the needle is withdrawn from the donor's vein and the blood-filled tube is sealed using a tube-heating sealer. The bag of blood now has a long blood-filled tube which is then heat-sealed in several places, usually around eight, and it is these segments or tails that are used for cross-match testing. The segments or tails are isolated from each other, and one can be cut from the tail without compromising the others or the blood in the bag itself.

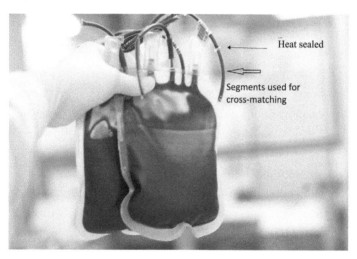

Heat sealed

Segments used for cross-matching

That segment, when cut from the main tube, is then cut open and the blood from it can be used in the cross-match or, if the donor is new to the transfusion service, it can be used to ABO and rhesus group the donor.

To remove the donor's plasma from the red cells, they are washed in saline, usually three times, and then suspended in saline.

The patient's serum can now be added to the washed

donor red cells, left for a short period of time depending upon the practice adopted by the laboratory, and then microscopically examined to determine if any agglutination has taken place. In most cases, a sea of free red cells will be observed, indicating compatibility between the patient and the donor, and the unit of blood can then be labelled for that patient. If, however, agglutination of the donor red cells is observed, the unit will be declared incompatible with the patient and further blood units will have to be cross-matched along with an investigation into what antibodies are present in the patient's serum causing the incompatibility.

The cross-match is carried out at room temperature and at 37°C. Room-temperature checks occasionally reveal the presence of antibodies that react better at these temperatures, although these antibodies rarely cause transfusion reactions. Nevertheless, such a unit would still be declared incompatible.

The tests at 37°C are, by far, the most important since they are mimicking the conditions which will be met by the donor red cells as they stream into the patient's veins.

The compatibility tests at 37°C are carried out by several different techniques sometimes involving enzymes and always including an antiglobulin test. These tests will detect the smaller antibodies (IgG) and might also reveal the presence of a weak antibody.

I will not attempt a further description of these techniques; they are complex and require a considerable degree of skill and understanding.

Suffice to comment that transfusion reactions are very rare as the compatibility tests employed are competent in detecting any antibodies the patient might have.

Very often the requested compatible blood is principally on standby for surgery and the patient might not need that blood transfused if there is no unexpected or excessive blood loss. When this occurs, the blood is returned to stock, the patient's label removed and it is then ready to be matched to another patient.

Since there are several tails left, that blood might well be cross-matched multiple times before it is used.

GROUP AND SAVE

When a patient has been assessed by the medical or surgical staff, they might consider that there is unlikely to be a requirement for standby blood and, in this event, they would simply ask for a 'Group and Save'.

A sample of the patient's clotted blood is sent to the blood bank with the request and the laboratory will ABO and rhesus group the patient and, the serum will be checked for the presence of blood group antibodies. If any antibodies are detected, the laboratory will have time to identify them and this will save time if a cross-match is later requested.

The patient's red cells are stored in a refrigerator and the serum is stored frozen and held for the duration of that patient's stay in hospital.

USE OF TYPE-SPECIFIC BLOOD

Occasionally, there is a requirement to give blood urgently, one where the medical staff feel that they cannot wait for blood to be cross-matched. In this instance, the laboratory will provide a rapid blood group for the patient and blood of the same ABO and rhesus group will be transfused to the patient. It is considered unlikely that any transfusion reaction will be experienced by the patient, so the risk being minimal is balanced against the critical outcome that might occur as a consequence of acute blood loss.

As medical and surgical innovative practices have progressed over the years, so the demand for blood has added pressure on the Transfusion Service to supply sufficient units to meet all demands.

A system introduced to address this issue is called 'Intraoperative cell salvage' and this equipment and technique is often used in a surgical setting where it is anticipated that the patient might suffer a substantial blood loss.

The equipment involved recovers the patient's spilled blood into a sterile collection vessel which contains an anticoagulant to ensure that it stays fluid.

It is then filtered to remove any particulates, centrifuged and washed in saline and, ultimately, re-infused to the patient.

This procedure is recommended where a patient's blood loss is likely to be substantial and it has several advantages. Cross-matched blood is not required so compatibility is not an issue.

Some Jehovah Witness patients object to being transfused with donor blood and might or might not consent to this intraoperative procedure.

The reader may wonder if subsequent bacterial contamination might be a problem, but there are very few, if any, reports of such an outcome.

The procedure has also been shown to be cost-effective.

There have been many attempts to manufacture an artificial blood substitute, one which could fulfil all the functions of the human red cell. A blood substitute would negate the need for cross-matching. It would remove the danger of blood-borne viral cross infection and, of course, the military would wholly embrace it. This has been the ambition of many biomedical researchers for a very long time and several oxygen-carrying blood substitutes have been manufactured and have progressed to clinical trials.

However, several problems have been encountered with these substitutes and, to date, no suitable alternative to human red cells has been found to be successful.

According to Grethlein,[46] several substitutes have been proposed and researched over a period of 70 years in an attempt to develop an ideal alternative to blood.

A number of perfluorocarbons (PFC) have been used but have all been withdrawn from use as the clinical trials gave rise to strokes, pulmonary surfactant damage and acute complement activation.

Other products such as recombinant haemoglobin, polymerised haemoglobin, conjugated bovine and human haemoglobin have all been trialled, but a suitable artificial substitute for red cell transfusion has proved particularly difficult and the use of donor red cells continues to be the safest product.

Many remote communities do not have ready access to blood bank laboratory services and often the urgent demand for blood grouping and cross-matching is simply not available. Before the emergency use of helicopters, these communities had to have provision made for blood grouping and transfusion when accidents or some other blood loss emergency arose.

To meet some of this end, very often Eldon cards were/are used. They were the invention of Knud Eldon, a Danish physician who devised these cards more than 40 years ago.

They have a shelf life of 24 months from the date of manufacture and contain four circles, comprising anti-A, anti-B, anti-D and a control. The antiserum is dried onto the card at manufacture and simply requires a small sample of the patient's blood to be added to each circle. There are also spaces for identification of the patient whose blood is being tested.

A full ABO and rhesus grouping can be read in two minutes.

These cards are ideal in a military setting where blood bank laboratories are a luxury that are simply not available. Army medics are likely to have blood packs at their disposal and with Eldon card results, type-specific blood transfusions can readily be given.

The Eldon Card is NATO approved and used by many armed forces in order to assist in the field.

New US studies have shown that it is crucial to obtain the correct blood type within 10–15 minutes. Consequently, urgent typing may be considered as essential.

There was a time when educationalists in the UK thought

CROSS-MATCHING, ETC.

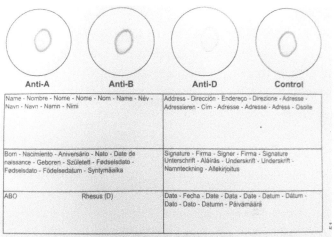

Eldon card before blood has been added

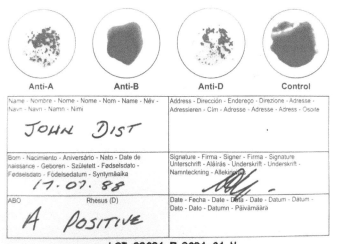

Eldon card after blood has been added

103

these cards would make the biology class more interesting for the students. However, taking into consideration blood-borne diseases and the cavalier manner often adopted by young teenagers, the exercise was soon abandoned. Nevertheless, they are still used in biology lessons in many countries.

Remote communities can have walking donors where members of the community have been blood grouped and can be called upon to donate where an urgent need arises. Sometimes Eldon cards were used to blood group volunteers in these small communities and a new app is currently being tested which will communicate one-to-one to secure more donors.

These cards will also help in the fight against rhesus disease in areas where there is a lack of awareness and treatment of the disease.

However, this practice is frowned upon in this scientifically advanced world since all donors need to be fully tested for blood-borne diseases and a simple Eldon card grouping cannot achieve this.

Nevertheless, these cards serve an important purpose and will, in many circumstances, save lives. Several NGO groups (non-governmental groups such as the Red Cross) are using Eldon Cards in disaster areas and refugee camps.

The following tale, while not related to blood groups, is worthy of recounting since it helps reveal that sometimes in pregnancy, the rather innocent young male must be awakened to certain facts of life and where discretion and confidentiality is of paramount importance.

For me it had been quite a long night. I was on call, having been out at the hospital for around four hours, and was just about to return home when a phone call advised me that an ante-partum haemorrhage was on her way in by ambulance and might urgently need some blood matched.

It was almost 4am and I was a little hungry, so I went across to one of the wards opposite the laboratory to make myself some tea and toast. The nursing staff in this ward always made us welcome through the night if we got hungry and I soon got the tea and toast organised.

There was a little sitting room which was next to the duty room, and I made myself comfortable with my tea and toast and quickly relaxed.

These two wards were set up for the admission of patients suffering a miscarriage and they had recently been refurbished. One of the issues with the refurbishment of that cluster of wards was that the walls were about as soundproof as paper and one could hear everything that was being said in the duty room, confidential or not.

As I sat enjoying my tea and toast, I could not help but hear voices as two people entered the duty room.

The anxiety in the young man's voice next door was unequivocal as he spoke to the staff nurse, expressing his concern and fear for his young wife.

The sister was trying to reassure him.

"She is going to be okay." she said quietly. "It is sad that she has lost the baby and she is going to find that hard but given time she will recover."

"It was terrible when it happened," he said quite loudly. "I thought that she was going to die!"

"Unfortunately, this happens to a lot of young women." The nurse was trying to calm him down. "I can assure you that she will be fine given time to get over the loss."

There was a silence for a few moments before the nurse continued.

"Anyway," she paused for a moment then continued again. "She's not nearly as bad as she was the last time she was in."

There was another long pause before the young man said with a quivering voice,

"What last time?"

I didn't wait to hear anything further.

TEN

MONOCLONAL ANTIBODIES

"Blood is the rose of a mysterious union."
Jim Morrison

Before the use of monoclonal antibodies, the antisera used by blood transfusion laboratories to determine donor and patient blood groups was obtained from individuals who had avid antibodies in their serum. These antibodies were usually collected from blood donor serum.

When required, a group B donor whose serum showed a very strong reaction with group A red cells would be selected and aliquots of that donor's serum (anti-A) would be made.

Similarly, a group A donor whose serum showed a very strong reaction with group B red cells would be selected and aliquots of that donor's serum (anti-B) would be made.

These aliquots would be distributed to hospital and transfusion centre blood banks for patient typing and donor typing.

In the USA, anti-A and anti-B antisera were acquired from volunteers who had agreed to be hyper-immunised.

To explain further, a group A volunteer would have a small volume of group B red cells transfused into a vein and a group B volunteer would have a small volume of group A red cells transfused into a vein. These red cells which were foreign to the recipient, would stimulate their immune system to produce more antibody and subsequent small incompatible red cells would further stimulate their immune system. This would continue until very potent anti-A and anti-B antibodies were present and, at this stage, the volunteer's serum could be used for guaranteed ABO blood typing.

These volunteers were, of course, handsomely paid by the commercial world and the USA companies involved in such antibody production sold their products throughout the world. This practice of commercially producing high-quality antibodies for blood grouping was not allowed in the UK.

In order to protect blood bank staff, any selected antisera would require to be fully checked for blood-borne diseases.

However, the modern world of blood banking has moved away from traditional human antisera which is polyclonal* and that antisera is now harvested from monoclones.**

The clones that are human-derived ABO antisera can be many and varied, and, consequently, such antisera are called 'polyclonal'. It was recognised, however, that some clones could secrete a single antibody and these antibodies were referred to as 'monoclonal'.

---

* Antibodies which are made up from many monoclonal cell sources.
** Copied antibodies which have a single genetic makeup as that of the original.

The thoughts of many researchers to isolate and artificially cultivate a single clone yielding a useful antibody became a burning ambition for those involved in antibody production.

At this time, the artificial cultivation of tissue cells was well established. Cells can divide and the number of times they can perform this growth function is genetically determined. However, some cell lines can be chemically or virally induced to continue dividing and this transformation and ability to divide indefinitely is referred to as 'a continuous cell line'.

These cell lines are cultivated in a tank which contains essential nutrients to keep the tissue cells alive. There are many advantages in cell science using cultivated cells. Proposed drug therapy, effects of toxic compounds and the study of carcinogenesis are all platforms available for study without resorting to animal use.

But don't be misled into thinking this is a stress-free technique that anyone can turn to. It is complex, extremely demanding in time, with sterility and procedural performance challenges. It is also capital-hungry, especially if failures are persistent. However, the rewards can be gratifying, especially when the cells secrete the desired antibody.

The first monoclonal antibodies were scientifically created by Köhler[47] and Milstein in 1975. César Milstein was an Argentinian biochemist who started work in the Laboratory of Molecular Biology, Cambridge, in 1963.

His passion was antibodies, and he had a vision of creating monoclonal antibodies that would lend themselves to novel medicines.

His knowledge and abilities were developed with his team at Cambridge, and they frequently published papers on the structure and diversity of antibodies, and during this period, he was working on myeloma cell fusions.

In 1973, he met Georges Köhler, a German biologist, and at this time, he was working on myeloma cell fusions with another colleague.

He invited Köhler to join him in Cambridge and, together, the two pursued their deep interest in developing monoclonal antibodies. They devised a process where mouse spleen cells were fused to a cell line created from mouse tumour cells. This newly created cell line is called a hybridoma and it could readily secrete monoclonal antibodies. This remarkable scientific breakthrough was done in the same laboratory where Francis Crick and James Watson discovered the structure of DNA in 1953.

The laboratory they were working in was not conducive to the artificial cultivation of living cells. It was a very crowded basement room where bacterial contamination of cell lines would be an everyday threat to their work.

When their paper was published in 1975, Abraham Karpas, Assistant Director of Research in the Department of Haematology University of Cambridge, wrote:

> *"It is not an exaggeration to describe César Milstein's contribution to science and medicine as the most important immunological advance of the century. His discovery of the method to produce monoclonal*

antibodies reinvented the field of immunology. The ability to make monoclonal antibodies at will in the test tube and in unlimited quantities, to any sort of antigen, whether an interesting chemical, infectious microorganism, cancer or normal cells, opened numerous new and unforeseen avenues for research, many with medical implications."

They reproduced their technique on seven separate occasions to prove that they now had a practical and effective system which many scientists, for a considerable number of years, had been seeking to achieve. Essentially, they had created an immortal cell line which could secrete an endless supply of identical antibodies.

However, there was a period of uncertain anxiety for the two researchers. Having proven to themselves that their technique was essentially reproducible, they submitted their paper to the journal *Nature*. Their next experimental run of the technique, the eighth, ended in failure, as did the following series, and some anxiety shrouded the research work. This continued for some months, one fusion failure after another, and they were faced with the distressing decision of having to withdraw their paper from publication.

However, one of their colleagues, Giovanni Galfré, traced the problem to an improperly prepared solution which was having a detrimental effect on the viability of the cells, and with that issue resolved and the technique working again the paper was cleared for publication.

Köhler and Milstein, along with Niels Jerne, a theoretician, were jointly awarded the Nobel Prize in Physiology or Medicine in 1984 for 'theories concerning the specificity and development and control of the immune system and the discovery of the principle for the production of monoclonal antibodies'.

Many drugs used in medicine are derived from monoclonal antibodies and these drugs now make up a large part of the medical drugs on the market today. In 2012, Humira,* a drug which is used for rheumatoid arthritis, had a revenue of $9.3 billion.

Monoclonal antibodies are also used widely in diagnostics, having the ability to accurately detect a range of conditions, both human and veterinarian.

Despite the fact that Milstein did foresee the huge potential of monoclonal antibodies in medicine, he did not patent the technique.

Now you will probably have guessed where this tale is taking us. Milstein and Köhler in 1975 made attempts to manufacture monoclonal anti-D but were not successful.

The Regional Blood Transfusion Centre based at Addenbrooke's Hospital was a short walk from Milstein's laboratory, where Douglas Voak was the Director. Milstein and Voak were joined by Steven Sacks, who had, along with Edwin Lennox, developed a monoclonal antibody which Voak was able to determine as anti-A. This antibody had been a serendipitous finding since it had not been the target objective. However, the avidity of this antibody was very poor but nevertheless exciting, since the researchers knew that they could, with further research manipulation, enhance that avidity. And, indeed, this was the case as a potent anti-A emerged from a second cell line some weeks later.

These findings transformed the entire blood-grouping world[48] as collections of human sera were no longer required and any worry of blood-borne diseases from human antisera disappeared. It was also, eventually, accepted that monoclonal antibodies are much more cost-effective compared to those from a human source.

In time, all other useful antibodies were generated as monoclonal antibodies and only very rarely is there a use for antibodies from a human source.

It is clear from the above that the impact of monoclonal antibodies on the blood-grouping world was immense and their potential for use in other medical sectors cannot be understated.

Manis et al[49], in 'Overview of therapeutic monoclonal antibodies' gives an excellent review of the outstanding contributions monoclonal antibodies have achieved in recent years. They state that, since the mid-1980s, more than 100 monoclonal-derived antibody-created drugs have been introduced for therapeutic use. These are used widely in cancer treatment in several different ways and for several immunological diseases. Indeed, a considerable number of diseases are now treated successfully with a host of monoclonal antibody-derived therapeutics.

All the above underlines how apposite the award of the Nobel Prize for Physiology or Medicine in 1984 was to Köhler and Milstein.

I have, at times, apologised for the occasional difficult and convoluted explanations in the book, but spare a thought for the unfortunate students who embarked upon courses developed in the medical field to strangle as many brain cells as possible.

The Advanced Blood Transfusion Course was established to allow the more ambitious students to further their careers in the discipline.

The series of lectures were to be given in an old Victorian college which was a complex assortment of classes and small lecture theatres.

The first challenge for the student was to find the lecture room and that was no easy task. The lecturer, a well-respected but short-tempered individual from a blood transfusion service centre allowed ten minutes after the scheduled start time before he got underway.

"I will start by covering all the topics we will be discussing and exploring in the coming months."

This particular lecturer was very knowledgeable on blood banking and he liked to show it.

For the students, his topics sounded more like a science-fiction catalogue; they ranged from one subject to another with titles and descriptions wholly foreign to them.

When he was in full verbal fantasy stride, the door opened and a young female stuck her head around the door. The lecturer stopped and stared at her.

"Sorry I'm late," she said, "just couldn't find the lecture theatre."

The lecturer said nothing but signalled her to come in and take a seat, which she did. He then jumped back into his harangue, delving into the depths and ambiguities of the blood-grouping world as he saw it. After a few more minutes the late-coming female stuck her hand in the air. The lecturer sighed and stopped.

"What!" he snapped.

"Sorry," she said awkwardly, "but I've come to the wrong lecture room."

"Where should you be?" Grumbled the annoyed lecturer.

"I should be at the Blood Transfusion Course."

The lecturer paused only briefly.

"Sit down, you stupid bitch!" he said unsympathetically.

It is unlikely that a lecturer would make such a comment in this day and age but in those earlier days, the lecturer had the authority.

ELEVEN

A MISCELLANY OF BLOOD GROUP INTEREST

"Blood alone moves the wheels of history."
Martin Luther

ANIMAL BLOOD GROUPS

Evolution, having equipped the human species with blood groups in the form of antigens on their red cells, probably saw every reason to also equip other species with a similar mechanism on their red cells.

Consequently, and as you might imagine, animals have blood groups not unlike those seen in the human species. Some of these groups have great similarities to the human groups and each species has its own characteristics; while similar to the human groups they are, in other respects, quite different.

We are recognised for our affection for domestic animals; mostly we look after them and seek to ensure their health is well cared for. When they are unwell, the occasional requirement for blood can arise and, within the veterinary world there can be a demand for blood typing and, of course, transfusion. Indeed, the demands in animal welfare, from the commercial-farming sector to the domestic setting, is significant.

To meet some of these needs, animal blood banks have been set up which can provide grouped and compatible units of blood for some animals. The Pet Blood Bank has supplied around 27,000 units for dog transfusions at the time of writing this book.

Nevertheless, perhaps we should take a look at our closest contemporaries in the animal world. Charles Darwin's theory of evolution revealing our close relationship with the primates  seems a good place to have a look at human and primate blood-group relationships.

Primate blood grouping has usually been carried out using monoclonal anti-A and anti-B, and according to Socha[50], chimpanzees have been primarily grouped as group A with a small number grouping as group O. Gorillas appear to be principally group B.

Baboons have been found to group as A, B and, on rare occasions, O.

However, their red cells do not always carry the antigens; these groupings are often only found in their tissues.

Virtually all animals have blood groups and there have been attempts to blood type in the avian world as well as sea creatures. Essentially, there will be no area where man hasn't attempted to blood group. If it has blood circulating, someone will have attempted to blood group it.

If we dip into marine life, not surprisingly, no one has, as of yet, set up any fish blood banks, but there has been no stopping research in trawling such a rich pool of life to retrieve something of blood group value. And, indeed, the common eel *Anguilla anguilla* was found to contain an excellent anti-H-like antibody in its serum. While it was a useful antibody, the common eel has very little blood and commercially obtaining sufficient blood to harvest the antibody was hardly practicable.

Not too far away from the eels mentioned above, the snails *Helix hortensis* and *Helix pomatia* have been found to contain a potent anti-A which is located in their albumin gland. This is a very worthwhile anti-A agglutinin and was, at one time, commercially farmed for use in the major automated blood-grouping equipment.

But bear in mind, the human immune system, if confronted with animal blood as a consequence of transfusion, would find that blood grossly incompatible and would immediately bring about the destruction of the transfused animal red cells.

But enough about animal blood types; human blood groups

are complicated enough without attempting to unravel the complexities of those in the animal world.

SEEDS AND PLANTS

The ability of seed extracts to agglutinate human red cells was recognised as early as the late nineteenth century and the volume of research since then into what can be extracted from seeds and plants is immense.

These extracts are generally referred to as lectins which are sugar-binding proteins that can bring about agglutination of particular cells.

The most significant lectin finding was that of George Bird,[51] who discovered that an extract from the seeds of *Dolichos biflorus* would specifically agglutinate A_1 and A_1B red cells without agglutinating A_2 or A_2B red cells. This was an important finding since human anti-A_1 is very weak and not very common, while the Dolichos extract was a strong reactor and freely available.

George Bird joined the British Army as a medic and was posted to India, where he was involved in trauma management. There he was accredited with establishing the first blood bank in India and he had developed a strong interest in lectins.

He, subsequently, showed that an extract from the peanut[52] *Arachis hypogea* contained anti-T, another very important finding in the blood bank world.

George was prolific in his research publications, most of which were related to lectins and their application in blood grouping.

There are several other seeds which can provide an excellent anti-A$_1$ and many can be found in the Vicia family.

An anti-B like lectin has been found in the fungus *Fomes fomentarius* which grows on birch trees mainly in the northern areas of Scotland. The extracted antibody-like anti-B is very weak and is not used for blood-grouping purposes.

It is of interest that the two plant extracts described above, anti-A$_1$ and anti-T, are difficult to find in human antisera. Another very useful antibody-like extract in plants is anti-H, which is found in the seeds of *Ulex europaeus* which grows all over the UK and is known as common gorse.

Anti-N can be extracted from the leaves of the plant *Vicia unijuga* and is an extremely useful extract.

Table 10. Antibody-like lectins commonly found in plants

Antibody	Where found	Useful?	Comment
Anti-A$_1$	*Dolichos biflorus* seeds	Very	Commonly used
	Albumin gland of snail	Yes	No longer used
	Vicia plants	No	Not used
Anti-B	*Fomes fomentarius*	No	Not used
Anti-H	*Ulex europaeus* seeds	Yes	Commonly used
	Eel serum	No	Not used
Anti-T	*Arachis hypogea* seeds	Yes	Commonly used
Anti-N	*Vicia unijuga* leaves	Yes	Often used

The research into what can be extracted from plants and seeds is on-going. Many seed extracts can show a strong agglutination with human red cells and most, from a blood-grouping perspective, are recorded as 'non-specific' since they do not agglutinate any specific blood group.

One seed showing such a reaction is the castor oil plant seed *Ricinus communis*. It strongly agglutinates the red cells of all human blood groups showing no blood group specificity whatsoever.

This seed is worthy of further mention, however, since it has truly remarkable properties other than its ability to agglutinate red cells.

The extracted oil from the seed has been used as an engine oil in aeroplanes, especially those with rotary engines.

It is probably best known medicinally for its properties as a laxative as it can readily ease a constipated bowel. Yet the oil is, in fact, poisonous and must be boiled to neutralise the toxin before it can be used medicinally.

The toxin extracted from this seed is ricin, and this is indeed, a particularly potent toxin. Compared to cyanide, ricin, if injected, is 6000 times more poisonous, requiring only 5 – 10 micrograms/Kg to bring about death and it has been used as a terrorist weapon.

In 1978, Georgi Markov, a Bulgarian writer and dissident, was stabbed in the back of his leg with an umbrella. The umbrella injected a minute pellet coated in ricin into his leg and he died a few days later. The man holding the umbrella was reputed to be a Bulgarian Secret Service agent. Other reports have been published where ricin has been used as a terrorist weapon.

A brighter side of ricin has been recognised as it has anti-cancer properties. Ricin is a ribosome-inactivating protein which destroys the cells by inhibiting protein synthesis and it induces the early death of the cancer cell by apoptosis.*

But while it has properties in bringing about the death of the cancer cell, that property has to be separated from the powerful toxic property that would kill the patient anyway, and so far, that has not been achieved.

During the nineties, the Government issued a letter with a questionnaire to all companies holding chemicals in order to determine who might be holding dangerous compounds that might be used by terrorists.

We received the document, and I was a bit worried as I read through the numerous pages. The only item in question for me was the Ricinus communis as we were holding several kilograms, all for research purposes.

So, I filled out the pages declaring our possession of this common lectin and about two weeks later I received a telephone call from a gentleman from Porton Down. He was keen to know just what we were doing with Ricinus communis and were we extracting ricin from the seeds. I explained our interests in trying to separate the two known fractions, etc. and we entered into a lengthy discussion on the properties of Ricinus communis other than those of a toxic nature. The man from the Ministry was extremely pleasant and we formed a short but useful friendship.

Another useful property of Ricinus communis?

---

* The programmed death of a cell.

WHO HAS THE SAME BLOOD GROUP AS YOU?

Blood group O

The Queen Elizabeth II, King Charles II, John Lennon, Marilyn Monroe, Kurt Cobain, Neil Armstrong, Al Capone, Dwight Eisenhower, Liam Gallagher, Charles Manson, Paul Newman.

Paul Newman   *Neil Armstrong*   *John Lennon*

Blood group A

Jimmy Carter, Richard Nixon, George Bush, Fidel Castro, Phil Collins, Angelina Jolie, Britney Spears.

Angelina Jolie   *George W Bush*   *Phil Collins*

Blood group B

Jack Nicholson, Johnny Depp, Leonardo DiCaprio, Mia Farrow, Paul McCartney, Freddie Mercury, Julia Roberts, Susan Saradon.

Jack Nicholson   *Julia Roberts*   *Leonardo DiCaprio*

Blood group AB

Jennifer Aniston, Meryl Streep, Barack Obama, Mick Jagger, Charles de Gaul, John F Kennedy.

Jennifer Aniston   *Meryl Streep*   *Barack Obama*

TWELVE

THE FUTURE: WHERE WILL IT TAKE US?

"To look into the mirror is to see the future, in blood and rubies."
Gregory Maguire

Currently there is a worldwide requirement for 85 million whole blood donations each year and less than half of this comes from the less developed countries where more than 75% of the population live.[53]

Despite this staggering number, it must be remembered that blood-borne pathogens present a persistent challenge to those trying to guarantee the safe use of blood. It is wholly recognised in medicine that blood and/or blood components should only be given where it is considered absolutely necessary.

There has been a move towards 'bloodless medicine' by many experts and, as has already been said, the use of intraoperative cell salvage equipment goes some way to achieving this.

The phases for this procedure are fairly simple: the shed

blood is sucked into the machine by a lumen and a second lumen adds heparinised saline as an anticoagulant. The collected heparinised blood is then passed through a filter and collected in a reservoir. The filter will remove unwanted particles such as white cells, platelets, free haemoglobin and the heparin. The collected red cells are concentrated to around 50–80% and are re-transfused to the patient within six hours.

Ashworth and Klein[54], give an excellent review of the published work on the subject and place the practice in a favourable light, concluding that the routine is safe and cost-effective in cardiac and orthopaedic surgery.

The use of allogeneic* blood transfusion has been associated with an increased risk of tumour recurrence, postoperative infection, acute lung injury, perioperative myocardial infarction, postoperative low-output cardiac failure and morbidity.

However, there will continue to be a need for urgent transfusions for many years to come where patients present with anaemia, dramatic blood loss, where the surgeons find it necessary to subject the body to the scalpel and where pregnant women haemorrhage unexpectedly.

Nevertheless, the present medical world is aware of the need to reduce dependence on donor blood and most hospitals have a policy where the use of blood or blood products is carefully thought through.

Further to this, advanced surgical procedures along with

---

* Acquired from individuals of the same species. In this case, blood.

new innovative practices often demand additional blood coverage and the requirement for blood could increase every year. The pressures on the blood transfusion services tends to mount every year.

There is always some wastage with blood. Not every pack is used and there is a constant effort by the services to cut this loss to a minimum. Blood units can be cross-matched for a patient and, when that patient's surgical or medical event is over, the unit may not have been required. Consequently, that unit of blood will be unlabelled and will be ready to be cross-matched for another patient.

This cycle can continue, and the unit may be matched for many patients.

A factor which will cut these losses is the shelf life given to the product.

The various blood transfusion services across the world might give a slightly different shelf life to their blood and product packs depending upon a number of values and standards set by that blood bank.

Generally, a 35 – 42 day shelf life is allotted to each unit of red cells, while a pack of platelets has seven days. Fresh Frozen Plasma is usually held for three years.

When donor blood was originally bled into glass bottles, the unit was given a 21 day shelf life. It was recognised very early that the solution the donor blood was stored in, would have the major effect on the life of that blood, and considerable research has been carried out over the years to enhance and promote the life of the stored red cell. As well as an anticoagulant, nutrients have gradually, over the years, been added and the 35 – 42 day shelf life generally meets the needs of most transfusion service units.

The COVID periods of lockdown and hospital difficulties have interrupted the routine of elective operations taking place and the demand for blood has certainly eased off during this period.

BLOOD SUBSTITUTES

While group O Rh-negative blood is considered a universal donor, an endless supply is simply not available. If, however, an inert effective solution could be manufactured to take the place of red cells to carry haemoglobin around the body and return carbon dioxide to the lungs, we could forget the worries of antigens and antibodies and, possibly, even the need for refrigeration and simply have bags of this solution available to transfuse the patient.

Thomas[55], around 150 years ago, proposed milk as a suitable substitute for blood, designating the alternative as 'Lacteal injections'. Of the three patients he treated, two died and one survived, and he attributed the deaths to causes other than the milk infusions.

Over many decades, there have been large financial resources ploughed into the search for a suitable product to replace the need for blood. There can be little dispute that a successful blood substitute would earn the patent owner significant sums of money as the demand would be colossal.

With all of that in mind, huge efforts over many years have been made in this direction and they have tended to be haemoglobin-based oxygen carriers (HBOC) and perflourocarbons (PFCs).

PFCs are biologically inert and can dissolve around 50 times more oxygen than blood plasma. However, they are not soluble in water and must be attached to an emulsifier so that they can be suspended in the circulation.

With haemoglobin-based substitutes, an *E. coli* is used which has the ability to produce human-like haemoglobin. An issue with this type of substitute is that the product lasts no more than 20–30 hours in the circulation.

So far, eleven substitutes have been manufactured and reached the stage of seeking approval from the appropriate medical regulatory body. Only three have been given that approval, one for veterinary purposes, one Russian but only accepted in Russia and Mexico, and one in South Africa where the withdrawal of that product is now being considered.

Fluosol-DA-20, manufactured by the Green Cross of Japan, was the first oxygen carrier to be approved by the FDA in USA. However, it was withdrawn in 1994 due to side effects experienced by the patients receiving it.

Many patients receiving these blood substitutes in clinical trials have shown side effects ranging from stroke incidents, elevated blood pressure, abdominal discomfort, capillary collapse, heart attacks and some brain problems.

It is very likely that some suitable product will be developed that meets all the necessary requirements, but that seems to be still on the distant horizon for the present.

So, the quest for the Holy Grail of blood substitutes remains frustratingly unfulfilled and we are faced with accepting human-transfused blood as the only acceptable replacement for excessive blood loss. We will have to tolerate the antigens that are not quite us and hope that those streaming into us do not aggravate our immune system to an angry response.

But, depending upon our physical state, we might be only too grateful to accept the precious gift of a unit of blood.

On 7th. November 2022, the NHS Blood and Transplant unit at Cambridge, along with the Universities of Bristol and Cambridge, Guy's and St Thomas' NHS Foundation Trust, the NIHR, Cambridge Clinical Research and Cambridge University Hospitals NHS Foundation Trust[57], reported on the successful culture and manufacture of human red blood cells which had been transfused to human volunteers.

This was the first ever report of human red blood cells, having been grown in a laboratory, and subsequently, transfused to another person in the RESTORE randomised controlled clinical trial. The cells had been grown from stem cells collected from a donor.

In their first report they state:

'If proved safe and effective, manufactured blood cells could in time revolutionise treatments for people with blood disorders such as sickle cell and rare blood types. It can be difficult to find enough well-matched donated blood for some people with these disorders.'

This work is at a very early stage and it will take some considerable time before it advances to general use. It is nevertheless, a hugely important step towards blood safety and availability, and its potential cannot be overstated.

EVOLVING TO IMMUNE CHAOS?

It can be argued that there are only three sets of circumstances that can bring about death:

1. Accidents, murder, war, suicide, etc.
2. Microbial, including bacterial, viral, protozoal, etc.
3. Immunogenic failure.

In view of the discussion throughout this book, the third entry here is of considerable interest to us. There is little doubt that we are dependent upon a fully functioning immune system, one that is being faithful and loyal and not being spiteful towards our healthy cells. We need our antibodies to be directed spåecifically at foreign antigens, not those that are self.

However, it would seem that there can be issues with the immune system where it cannot always tell what is self and non-self, what are healthy cells and what are not, and it might consequently, start directing antibodies to damage healthy cells.

So, what issues will our body encounter if our immune system starts to fail or become confused, and specifically, what disorders will we be faced with.

It is already well established that the autoimmune disorders, as described above, do occur and there is considerable evidence that these disorders can also be associated with malignancy as well as other complaints.

The following diseases are associated with autoimmune disease:

Type 1 diabetes	MS
Rheumatoid arthritis	Myasthenia gravis
Systemic Lupus Erythromatosis (SLE)	Pernicious anaemia
Crohn's disease	Vasculitis
Celiac disease	Guillain-Barre syndrome
Ulcerative colitis	Psoriasis
Grave's disease	Addison's disease
Hashimoto's thyroiditis	Auto-immune haemolytic anaemia
Immune thrombocytopenia	

I note here only a small number of conditions that can fall into this group.

BUT WHERE IS EVOLUTION TAKING US?

In this book I have discussed antigens and antibodies endlessly and in some detail, and must wonder where progressive evolution will lead us.

Graves[56] et al, detail their views on natural selection promoting antigenic evolvability and suggest that their findings in pathogen evolution provide evidence that molecular mechanisms that enhance evolvability of surface antigens are an evolutionary adaption.

They do point out that the hypothesis that 'natural selection shapes the ability of a population to evolve' is highly controversial due to a lack of evidence.

But, if we accept that evolution is inevitable, is this progression partly driven through a re-shaping of the antigens and, perhaps, the creation of new antigens?

Man is, by far, the most advanced of the species on the planet. Evolution has dragged him from a primitive genus to a position of control and authority on the planet. Many researches link antigenic generation and mutation with evolution and, if we accept that man's antigens are partially responsible for the sophistication that separates him from other primates, we may also have to accept that this may bring unease on the consequences of this success.

If antigenic expression and generation is a constantly enduring conversion and creation to successfully evolve, this can only, ultimately, challenge the capability of the immune system. An overabundance of antigens created to constantly improve our capabilities and proficiencies so that we are superior to all other animals on the planet might prove to be the final challenge to bring confusion to the immune system. It might, ultimately, not have the capability of recognising self from non-self and, at this point, we would be in self-destruct mode.

But maybe no need to over concern ourselves yet; these thoughts on a terminal evolution will perhaps be a million years away, I hope.

REFERENCES

1   Landsteiner K: *On Agglutination of Normal Human Blood.* Wein. klin. Wschr., 14, 1132 (1901)

2   Decastello A, Sturli A: *Uber die isoagglutinine im serum gesunder und kranker memschen.* Munch. Med Wschr., 1090 (1902).

3   Prokop O, Uhlenbruck G: *Human Blood and Serum Groups.* MaClaren & Sons (1969).

4   Race RR, Sanger R: *Blood Groups in Man.* Blackwell Scientific Publications (1950).

5   Daniels G: *Human Blood Groups.* Published by Blackwell Science (1995).

6   NHS Blood and Transplant. Blood Types.

7   Average distribution of blood types in the United States as of 2021. Statista 2021.

8   Levine P, Stetson RE: 'An unusual case of intragroup agglutination'. JAMA. **113** (2): 126–7. doi:10.1001/jama.1939.72800270002007a.(1939).

9   Landsteiner K, Wiener AS: 'Studies on an agglutinogen (Rh) in human blood reacting with Anti-rhesus sera and with human isoantibodies'. J Exp Med. **74** (4): 309–320. doi:10.1084/jem.74.4.309. PMC 2135190. PMID 19871137. (1941).

10 Clarke CA, Sheppard PM: 'Prevention of rhesus haemolytic disease'. Lancet II 343. (1965).

11 Howard H, Martlew V, et al: 'Consequences for fetus and

neonate of maternal red cell allo-immunization'. Arch Dis Child Fetal Neonate Ed. Jan 78(1), F62–F66 (1998).

12 Landsteiner P, Levine P: 'A new agglutinable factor differentiating individual human bloods'. Proc. Soc. Exp. Biol. New York. 24: 600–602. (1927.)

13 Landsteiner P, Levine P: 'Further observations on individual differences of human blood'. Proc. Soc. Exp. Biol. New York. 24: 941–942. (1927.)

14 Callender S, Race RR and Paykoc ZV: 'Hypersensitivity to Transfused Blood'. Br. Med. J. ii: 83. (1945.)

15 Coombs RRA, Mourant AE and Race RR: 'In-vivo isosensitisation of red cells in babies with haemolytic disease'. Lancet. i. 264–266. (1946.)

16 Mourant AE: 'A new human blood group antigen of frequent occurrence'. Nature; 17 (158): 237. (1946.)

17 Cutbush M, Mollison PL and Parkin DM: 'A new human blood group'. Nature. 165. 188–189. (1950.)

18 Allen FH, Diamond LK and Niedziela B: 'A new blood group antigen'. Nature. 167:482. (1951.)

19 Schaer KF: 'Charakter, Blutgruppe und Konstitition'. Rascher, Zurich. (1941.)

20 Bohmer K: 'Blutgruppen und Verbrechen'. Dtsch. Zschr. Gerichtl. Med., 9, 426. (1927.)

21 Palmieri VM: 'Ricerche di biologia criminale'. I. La distribuzion dei gruppi sanguigni traiciminali alienate Nuova riv. Clin. psichiatr. 2. 155. (1929.)

22 Kanazawa M: 'ABO Blood Type and Personality Traits: Evidence from Large-scale Surveys in Japan'. Researchgate.net. DOI:10.31124/advance. 12410228.v1. (2020.)

23 Asgari O: 'Examination of the Impact of Blood Groups on Group Participation. Journal of Economics', Marketing and Management. 3(2). pp. 9–20. (2015.)

24 Gibson JR, Harrison GA, Clarke VA, et al: 'IQ and ABO blood groups'. Nature 246:498–500. (1973.)

25 Beardmore JA, Karimi-Booshehri F: 'ABO genes are differentially distributed in socioeconomic groups in England'. Nature: 303.522–524. (1983.)

26 Nomi T and Besher A: *You Are Your Blood Type.* New York, NY, Pocket Books. (1988.)

27 Kanazawa M: 'Relationship between ABO Blood Type and Personality in a Large-Scale Survey in Japan'. Int. J. of Psy. And Behav. Sc. (2021.)

28 Evans R: 'Japan and Blood Types: Does it Determine Personalities?' BBC News. (2012.)

29 Hakamori S: 'Fucolipids and blood group lipids in normal and tumour tissue'. Prog. Biochem. Pharmacol. 10: 167–196. (1975.)

30 Doughty BR: 'The changes in ABO blood group frequency within a mediaeval English population'. Med Lab Sci **34**:351–354.

31 Berger SA, Young NA, and Edberg SC: 'Relationship between infectious diseases and human blood type'. Eur J Clin Microbiol Infect Dis. 8: 681–689. (1989.)

32 Pourali F, Afshari M, Alizadeh-Navei R, Javidnia J, Moosazedeh M and Messaami A: 'Relationship between blood group and risk of infection and death in COVID-19: a live meta-analysis'. New Microbes and New Infections Vol. 37. (Sept 2020.)

33 Taha SAH, Osman MEM, Abdoelkarim EAA, Holie MA, Elbasheir MM, Abuzeid NMK, Al-Thobaiti SA, Fadul SB, Konozy EHE: 'Individuals with Rh-positive but not Rh-negative blood group are more vulnerable to SARS-CoV-2 infection: demographics and trend study on COVID-19 cases in Sudan'. New Microbes and New Infections. Vol. 38. (Nov 2020)

34 Mourant AE et al: *The Distribution of the Human Blood Groups and Other Polymorphisms*, 2nd ed. (1976.)

35 Brown ES: 'Distribution of the ABO and Rhesus (D) blood groups in the North of Scotland'. Heredity. 20 289–303. (1965.)

36 Cartwright RA and Milne GR: 'ABO and Rhesus (D) blood group results from the Isle of Mull'. Annals of Human Biology. 3. No. 3. 275–277. (1976.)

37 Newman S: *Newman's Concordance.*

38 Bull WT: 'On the intravenous injection of saline solutions as a substitute for transfusion of blood'. Med. Rec. 25: 6–8. (1884.)

39 Hustin A: 'Principe d'une nouvelle methode de transfusion muqueuse'. J. Med Brux. 12. 436–439. (1914.)

40 Shamov VN and Kostyukov MKH: 'By studying homoplasty a corpse – a blood transfusion from a corpse'. Khirurgiia arkhiv. 18 (1-4): 184–195. (1929.)

41 Agote L: 'Nueva procedimento para la transfusion de sangre'. An. Inst. Modelo clin Med 1:25. (1915.)

42 Dunsford I, Bowley CC, Hutchison AM, Thomson JS, Sanger R and Race RR: 'A Human Blood-Group Chimera'. Br Med J 2:81. (1953.)

43 Owen RD: 'Immunogenic consequences of vascular anastomoses between bovine twins'. Ibid. 102. 400. (1945.)

44 Seyfried H, Walewska I and Werblinska B: 'Unusual inheritance of ABO group in a family with weak B antigens'. Vox Sang., 9, 268–277. (1964.)

45 Bhende YM, Deshpande CK, Bhatia HM, Sanger R, Race RR, Morgan WTJ and Watkins WM: 'A "New" Blood Group Character Related to the ABO System'. The Lancet. 1: 903–904. (1952.)

46 Grethlein SJ: 'Blood Substitutes. Drugs and Diseases', Medscape. Dec. (2018.)

47 Köhler G and Milstein C: 'Continuous cultures of fused cells secreting antibody of predefined specificity'. Nature 256, 495–497. (1975.)

48 Voak D, Lennox E, Sacks S, Milstein C and Darnborough J: 'Monoclonal anti-A and anti-B: development as cost-effective agents'. Med Lab Sci; 39(2): 109–122. (1982.)

49 Manis JP, Furst DE, Tirnauer JS and Feldweg AM: 'Overview

of therapeutic monoclonal antibodies'. UpToDate. (2021.)

50 Socha WW: 'Blood groups of pygmy and common chimpanzees'. The pygmy chimpanzee. 13-4.1 Springer, Boston, MA. (1984.)

51 Bird G: 'Relationship of the Blood Sub-Groups A1, A2 and A1B A2B to Haemagglutinins present in the Seeds of Dolichos biflorus'. Chemistry, Medicine. Nature. (1952.)

52 Bird G: 'Anti-T in Peanuts'. Vox Sang. Nov–Dec. 748–749. (1964.)

53 Seifried E and Muller MM: 'The present and future of Transfusion Medicine'. Blood Transfusion. Oct; 9(4): 371–376. (2011.)

54 Ashworth A and Klein AA: 'Cell salvage as part of a blood conservation strategy in anaesthesia'. British Journal of Anaesthesia. Vol. 105. Issue 4. 401–416. (2010.)

55 Thomas TG: 'The intravenous injection of milk as a substitute for the transfusion of blood'. NY State J Med. 47: 449–465. (1878.)

56 Graves CJ, Ros VI, Stevenson B, Sniegowsky PD and Brisson D: 'Natural Selection Promotes Antigenic Evolvability'. PLoS Pathog. Nov. 9(11). (2013.)

57 First ever clinical trial of laboratory grown red blood cells being transfused into another person. Press release by NHS Blood and Transplant. Nov. (2022).